SIDE *by* SIDES
PRESTWICK HOUSE, INC.

CANTERBURY
TALES

GEOFFREY CHAUCER

An abridged version

of Chaucer's original

on the left and a

modern rendering

on the right

PH
PRESTWICK
H O U S E
INCORPORATED

P.O. Box 658 • Clayton, DE 19938
Tel: 1.800.932.4593
Web site: www.prestwickhouse.com

ISBN: 978-1-58049-520-2
Copyright ©1997 by Prestwick House, Inc.

Canterbury Tales

Table of Contents

INTRODUCTION. 6

THE GENERAL PROLOGUE 10

THE NUN'S PRIEST'S PROLOGUE. 56

THE NUN'S PRIEST'S TALE. 58

THE KNIGHT'S TALE 82

THE PARDONER'S TALE 160

THE WIFE OF BATH'S PROLOGUE. 182

THE TALE OF THE WIFE OF BATH 188

Introduction

Geoffrey Chaucer 1343 - 1400

Chaucer's father, an influential wine merchant, was able to secure Geoffrey a position as a page in a household connected to King Edward III. While Chaucer's duties as a page were humble, they allowed him the opportunity to view the ruling aristocracy, thus broadening his knowledge of the various classes of society. While serving in the English army, Chaucer was captured and held prisoner in France. After his release, he held a number of government positions. While in his twenties, Chaucer began writing poetry, and he continued to write throughout his life.

Canterbury, located about fifty miles southeast of London, was a favorite destination for pilgrims. In fact, Chaucer himself made a pilgrimage to Canterbury. While he did not set out on the pilgrimage looking for material to use in his writing, he was so impressed by the mix of company that he had met at the Tabard Inn, that he was inspired to write what was to become his masterpiece.

Structure of The Canterbury Tales

The Canterbury Tales is a frame story in that it is a story that includes within it other stories. The frame in this case is the story of a pilgrimage to Canterbury made by twenty-nine pilgrims. Within the frame are twenty-four individual stories told by the pilgrims. The stories told by the pilgrims are familiar tales, but Chaucer's retelling is considered masterful.

The pilgrims themselves are described in the General Prologue. In the Prologue, we see that the personality of each pilgrim is unique, but the character traits they exhibit are universal. People from three main segments of medieval society are brought together through the vehicle of the pilgrimage: church people, nobility, and common people and/or tradesmen. In this regard, one critic said *The Canterbury Tales* "presents a cavalcade of fourteenth century life."

A Note On Chaucer Text

The modern verse edition in this text is an abridgement of selections from *Canterbury Tales Rendered into Modern English* by J. U. Nicolson. You will note in comparing Chaucer's original text with Nicolson's version that both are in verse in that they both employ meter and rhyming couplets. To keep their meter and sound pattern, both writers frequently used unusual sentence construction, as you will note in the excerpt below.

Bifil that in that seson on a day,	Befell that, in that season, on a day
in Southwerk at the Tabard as I lay,	In Southwark, at the Tabard, as I lay
Redy to wenden on my pilgrymage	Ready to start upon my pilgrimage
To Caunterbury with ful devout corage,	To Canterbury, full of devout homage,
At nyght were come into that hostelrye	There came at nightfall to that hostelry
Wel nyne and twenty in a compaignye,	Some nine and twenty in a company
Of sondry folk by aventure yfalle	Of sundry persons who had chanced to fall
In felaweshipe, and pilgrimes were they alle,	In fellowship, and pilgrims were they all
That toward Caunterbury wolden ryde.	That toward Canterbury town would ride.
The chambres and the stables weren wyde,	The rooms and stables spacious were and wide,
And wel we weren esed atte beste.	And well we there were eased, and of the best.
And shortly, whan the sonne was to reste,	And briefly, when the sun had gone to rest,
So hadde I spoken with hem everichon	So had I spoken with them, every one,
That I was of hir felaweshipe anon,	That I was of their fellowship anon,
And made forward erly for to ryse,	And made agreement that we'd early rise
To take oure wey ther as I yow devyse	

To take the road, as you I will apprise.

In most instances, Nicolson was able to make his verse-rendering work well, in that he was able to keep the poem's meter and rhyme scheme while still conveying Chaucer's original meaning. In a few places, however, Nicolson had to modify Chaucer's meaning in order to keep the meter and rhyme pattern. When we put Nicolson's verse into prose, we went back to Chaucer's original if a difference in meaning existed between the two. If at this point, some students wonder why Nicolson bothered rendering *The Canterbury Tales* into verse, rather than writing it in prose, we think a quick comparison of his verse and our prose rendition quickly answers that point. Clearly, Nicolson's verse falls more pleasantly on the ear than our prose rendering, and better captures the spirit of the original than any prose rendering could.

He was the finest beggar of his house;
A certain district being farmed to him,
None of his brethren dared approach its rim;
For though a widow had no shoes to show,
So pleasant was his *In principio*,
He always got a farthing ere he went.
He lived by pickings, it is evident.

And he could romp as well as any whelp.
For he was not like a cloisterer,
With threadbare cope as is the poor scholar,
But he was like a lord or like a pope.
Of double worsted was his semi-cope,
That rounded like a bell, as you may guess.
He lisped a little, out of wantonness,
To make his English soft upon his tongue;
And in his harping, after he had sung,
His two eyes twinkled in his head as bright

As do the stars within the frosty night.
This worthy limiter was named Hubert.

He was the best beggar in his order so he had an assigned district that none of the other begging friars dared to enter. When he began his speech, "In the beginning," he was so persuasive that even a poor widow without shoes gave him a donation. He got money wherever he went and he lived well from his donations.

He could run around as well as any young person. For he was not, like some monks, secluded in a monastery with the threadbare robe of a poor scholar. Rather he was like a lord or like a pope with his robe that went around his stomach like a bell. To make his words sound softer he purposely lisped a little. And after he finished singing and playing the harp, his eyes twinkled as bright as any stars on a frosty night. This worthy limiter was named Hubert.

Points to Remember

Because any prose rendering of Chaucer is only a pale imitation, we encourage the student to begin by reading the verse selection and only referring to the prose when he or she is stuck. In so doing, the student should keep these points in mind.

1. Students who have not yet studied the Middle Ages may not have the knowledge to see the work in its historical context, particularly in regard to the church and the clergy. While we have added notes where appropriate, the student may wish to consult an encyclopedia or history text for background information.

2. When reading poetry, read from punctuation mark to punctuation mark. DO NOT stop at the end of a line unless there is a punctuation mark there. Pause one beat for a comma and two beats for period or semi-colon.

3. Occasionally, Nicolson will use a word which will be completely unfamiliar to you. In most cases, the meaning will be revealed by its context.

Setting and Context

The story opens at the Tabard Inn in Southwark. Southwark is a town fourteen miles from London where pilgrims meet to begin the journey to Canterbury. It has been a long winter, but with the arrival of spring it is time to make a religious pilgrimage. While the trip has a religious shrine as its destination, the pilgrimage will not be without its social aspects.

In Medieval times, the Catholic church, which was for all practical purposes the only religion in Europe prior to the Reformation, played an important part in everyone's life. Daily life could be terribly hard, and sometimes all that would make it bearable was the thought of a pleasant afterlife with God in heaven. Consequently, after the king and the nobility, the church was the third most powerful institution in this society. We will see in the prologue that within the church there is a social class hierarchy of roles and positions. For example, the monk obviously comes from a higher social class than the pardoner.

While Chaucer attacked the abuses in the Church and its wayward ministers in *The Canterbury Tales*, he, too, was a strong believer and supporter of the Church and its teachings.

The selections in this edition come from the International Collectors Library edition of *Canterbury Tales: Rendered into Modern English* by J. U. Nicolson, published 1934.

The General Prologue

WHEN APRIL WITH his showers sweet with fruit
The drought of March has pierced unto the root
And bathed each vein with liquor that has power
To generate therein and sire the flower;
5   When Zephyr also has, with his sweet breath,
Quickened again, in every holt and heath,
The tender shoots and buds, and the young sun
Into the Ram one half his course has run,
And many little birds make melody
10   That sleep through all the night with open eye
(So Nature pricks them on to ramp and rage)—
Then do folk long to go on pilgrimage,
And palmers to go seeking out strange strands,
To distant shrines well known in sundry lands.
15   And specially from every shire's end
Of England they to Canterbury wend,
The holy blessed martyr there to seek
Who helped them when they lay so ill and weak.

Befell that, in that season, on a day
20   In Southwark, at the Tabard, as I lay
Ready to start upon my pilgrimage
To Canterbury, full of devout homage,
There came at nightfall to that hostelry
Some nine and twenty in a company
25   Of sundry persons who had chanced to fall
In fellowship, and pilgrims were they all
That toward Canterbury town would ride.

The General Prologue

When the sweet showers of April have pierced the roots made dry by the drought of March and have bathed each root with a liquid that has the power to bring forth the flower; when the west wind with his sweet breath has also roused the tender buds in every grove and field, and the young sun has run one-half its course, and many little birds that sleep through all the night with open eye now make melody, then folks long to go on a pilgrimage, and pilgrims go to seek out foreign shores and to travel to distant well-known shrines. And, especially, from every town of England they go to Canterbury to seek the holy blessed martyr there, who helped them when they lay so ill and weak.

So it was that on a day in that season, in Southwark, at the Tabard Inn, as I, full of devout homage, made ready to start upon my pilgrimage to Canterbury. There came that night to the hotel twenty-nine people. These people who had happened to fall into a fellowship, were all pilgrims on their way to Canterbury town.

The rooms and stables spacious were and wide,
And well we there were eased, and of the best.
30   And briefly, when the sun had gone to rest,
So had I spoken with them, every one,
That I was of their fellowship anon,
And made agreement that we'd early rise
To take the road, as you I will apprise.
35   But none the less, whilst I have time and space,
Before yet farther in this tale I pace,
It seems to me accordant with reason
To inform you of the state of every one
Of all of these, as it appeared to me,
40   And who they were, and what was their degree,
And even how arrayed there at the inn;
And with a knight thus will I first begin.

The Knight

A knight there was, and he a worthy man,
Who, from the moment that he first began
To ride about the world, loved chivalry,
Truth, honour, freedom and all courtesy.
5   At Alexandria, he, when it was won;
Of mortal battles he had fought fifteen,
And he'd fought for our faith at Tramissene
And always won he sovereign fame for prize.
Though so illustrious, he was very wise
10   And bore himself as meekly as a maid.
He never yet had any vileness said,
In all his life, to whatsoever wight.
He was a truly perfect, gentle knight.
But now, to tell you all of his array,
15   His steeds were good, but yet he was not gay.
Of simple fustian wore he a jupon
Sadly discoloured by his habergeon;
For he had lately come from his voyage
And now was going on this pilgrimage.

The rooms and stables were spacious and wide, of the best, and we rested well there. And when the sun had gone down, I had spoken with each of them briefly and said that I was a pilgrim as well. Afterwards we made an agreement to rise early the next morning and begin our journey. But while I have time and space, and before I go any farther in this story, it seems to make good sense to give you some information about each person as they appeared to me; who they were, and what was their station in life, as well as how they were dressed; and with a knight I will begin.

The Knight

There was a knight, he was a worthy man, who, from the time that he first began to ride about the world, loved chivalry, truth, honor, freedom, and courtesy. He was at Alexandria when it was won and he had fought fifteen deadly battles. He also fought for Christianity at Tramissene. In each battle he fought, he won the greatest fame. Though very celebrated, he was also wise, and he acted as humble and meekly as a maiden. No matter what, he never spoke out of anger. He was truly a perfect and gentle knight. But now I'll mention the things he wore; while his horses were good, he was not showy. His simple tunic was rust-stained from his coat of armor because he had recently returned from a voyage before going on this pilgrimage.

The Squire

With him there was his son, a youthful squire,
A lover and a lusty bachelor,
With locks well curled, as if they'd laid in press.
Some twenty years of age he was, I guess.
5   In stature he was of an average length,
Wondrously active, aye, and great of strength.
He'd ridden sometime with the cavalry
In Flanders, in Artois, and Picardy,
And borne him well within that little space
10   In hope to win thereby his lady's grace.
Prinked out he was, as if he were a mead,
All full of fresh-cut flowers white and red.
Singing he was, or fluting, all the day;
He was as fresh as is the month of May.
15   Short was his gown, with sleeves both long and wide.
Well could he sit on horse, and fairly ride.
He could make songs and words thereto indite,
Joust, and dance too, as well as sketch and write.
So hot he loved that, while night told her tale,
20   He slept no more than does a nightingale.
Courteous he, and humble, willing and able,
And carved before his father at the table.

The Squire

With him was his son, a young Squire, a lover and lusty aspiring knight, whose curly hair appeared as if it had been pressed. He was about twenty years of age, I guess. In stature he was of average height and very athletic; he possessed great strength, and he had once served with the cavalry in Flanders, Artois, and Picardy. Considering his youth, he carried himself well in hopes of winning his lady's favor. He was embroidered like a meadow full of white and red fresh cut flowers. Singing and playing the flute all day, he was as fresh as the month of May. He wore a short robe with long, wide sleeves. He looked good on his horse and he rode it well. He could write songs and compose verse, joust and dance, too, as well as sketch and write.

He searched for love so much at night that he slept no more than does a nightingale. He was courteous, modest, and capable, as he carved for his father at the table.

The Yeoman

A yeoman had he, nor more servants, no,
At that time, for he chose to travel so;
And he was clad in coat and hood of green.
A sheaf of peacock arrows bright and keen
5   Under his belt he bore right carefully
(Well could he keep his tackle yeomanly:
His arrows had no draggled feathers low),
And in his hand he bore a mighty bow.
A cropped head had he and a sun-browned face.
10 Of woodcraft knew he all the useful ways.
Upon his arm he bore a bracer gay,
And at one side a sword and buckler, yea,
And at the other side a dagger bright,
Well sheathed and sharp as spear point in the light;
15 On breast a Christopher of silver sheen.
He bore a horn in baldric all of green;
A forester he truly was, I guess.

The Prioress

There was also a nun, a prioress,
Who, in her smiling, modest was and coy;
Her greatest oath was but "By Saint Eloy!"
And she was known as Madam Eglantine.
5   Full well she sang the services divine
Intoning through her nose, becomingly;
And fair she spoke her French, and fluently,
At table she had been well taught withal,
And never from her lips let morsels fall,
10 Nor dipped her fingers deep in sauce, but ate
With so much care the food upon her plate
That never driblet fell upon her breast.
In courtesy she had delight and zest.
Her upper lip was always wiped so clean
15 That in her cup was no iota seen

The Yeoman

The knight had a yeoman and no other servants, for at that time he preferred to travel so. The yeoman was wearing a coat and hood of green. Under his belt he carefully carried a bunch of bright, sharp peacock arrows. (He kept his equipment in good shape; his arrows did not have any ragged feathers). And in his hand he carried a mighty bow. He wore a short haircut, and his skin was tan. He knew all the useful ways of woodcraft. Upon his arm he wore a wristguard, and on one side a sword and shield, and on the other side, a fine dagger that was well sheathed and as sharp as the point of any spear. On his chest he wore a silver St. Christopher medal, and he carried a horn with a green strap. He was truly a forester, I guess.

The Prioress

There was also a nun, a prioress, whose smile was sincere and mild. Her greatest oath was, "By Saint Eloy!" She was known as Madam Eglantine. She sang the holy service very well, and she spoke French fluently and elegantly. At meals, she was so well-mannered that she never let crumbs fall from her lips. She took great delight and interest in good manners. She kept her upper lip so clean that you could see no trace of grease in her cup. She had a very pleasant and amiable disposition.

17

Of grease, when she had drunk her draught of wine.
She was right pleasant, amiable—in short.
But, to say something of her moral sense,
She was so charitable and piteous
20   That she would weep if she but saw a mouse
Caught in a trap, though it were dead or bled.
She had some little dogs, too, that she fed

On roasted flesh, or milk and fine white bread.
But sore she'd weep if one of them were dead,
25   Or if men smote it with a rod to smart:
For pity ruled her, and her tender heart.
Right decorous her pleated wimple was;
Her nose was fine; her eyes were blue as glass;
Her mouth was small and therewith soft and red;
30   But certainly she had a fair forehead;
It was almost a full span broad, I own,
For, truth to tell, she was not undergrown.
Neat was her cloak, as I was well aware.
Of coral small about her arm she'd bear
35   A string of beads and gauded all with green;
And therefrom hung a brooch of golden sheen
Whereon there was first written a crowned "A,"
And under, *Amor Vincit Omnia.*

But to speak of her inner nature, it must be said that she was so charitable and merciful that she would weep if she saw a mouse caught in a trap. She had some little dogs that she fed cooked meat or milk and fine white bread. She would cry if a dog died, or if she saw men hit one with a stick because pity ruled her and her tender heart. Her pleated veil was in good taste; her nose was thin; her eyes were as blue as glass; her mouth was small, soft, and red; but she certainly had an attractive forehead; it was as broad as one's hand, I say, for to tell the truth she was not small. I was well aware that her cloak was neat, and she wore a rosary chain with green division beads; and from the rosary chain hung a bright gold brooch on which was written a crowned "A" and under it, Love Conquers All.

The Monk

Note: When not doing manual labor, the monks of the order of St. Benedict devote their lives to prayer and study. Much of this prayer and study is done in the monk's bare, simple room called a cell. The chief man in a monastery is called an abbot. While monastic orders require their members to take vows of chastity and poverty, Chaucer suggests that many monks and friars frequently forgot both vows. The monk's and friar's profiles that follow are from the *Prologue*.

    A monk there was, one made for mastery,
An outrider, who loved his venery;
A manly man, to be an abbot able.
Full many a blooded horse had he in stable:
5   And when he rode men might his bridle hear
A-jingling in the whistling wind as clear,
Aye, and as loud as does the chapel bell
Where this brave monk was master of the cell.
The rule of Maurice or Saint Benedict,
10   By reason it was old and somewhat strict,
This said monk let such old things slowly pace
And followed new-world manners in their place.
He cared not for that text a clean-plucked hen
Which holds that hunters are not holy men
15   Nor that a monk, when he is cloisterless,
Is like unto a fish that's waterless;
That is to say, a monk out of his cloister.
But this same text he held not worth an oyster;
And I said his opinion was right good.
20   What? Should he study as a madman would
Upon a book in cloister cell? Or yet
Go labour with his hands and swink and sweat,
As Austin bids? How shall the world be served?
Let Austin have his toil to him reserved.
25   Therefore he was a rider day and night;
Greyhounds he had, as swift as birds in flight.

The Monk

There was a monk on this pilgrimage, one who was born to lead, one who loved hunting. He was a manly man and a likely candidate for abbot. He had many fine horses in his stable, and when he rode about, one could hear his bridle, which was decorated with fine bells, jingling as loudly in the wind as the chapel bells at his monastery.

Because the rules governing the monks in the Order of Saint Benedict were old and somewhat strict, this monk let those old rules slowly pass away and followed the new-world manners instead. He cared not a clean-plucked hen for any book that said hunters are not holy men, nor that a monk outside his cloister is like a fish out of water. He said that a book that said these things was not worth an oyster, and I said his opinion was a good one.

What should we expect of him? Should we expect that like some madman he should lock himself in his small, bare room reading books? Or, worse yet, do manual labor and slave and sweat as St. Augustine instructs? How will that serve the world? Let St. Augustine reserve that work for himself. Therefore, he was a rider day and night; he had greyhounds that were as swift as birds in flight.

Since riding and the hunting of the hare
Were all his love, for no cost would he spare.
I saw his sleeves were decorated at the hand
30   With fur of grey, the finest in the land;
Also, to fasten hood beneath his chin,
He had of good wrought gold a curious pin:
A love-knot in the larger end there was.
His head was bald and shone like any glass
35   And smooth as one anointed was his face.
Fat was this lord, he stood in goodly case.
His bulging eyes he rolled about, and hot
They gleamed and red, like fire beneath a pot;
His boots were soft; his horse of great estate.
40   Now certainly he was a fine prelate:
He was not pale as some poor wasted ghost.
A fat swan, loved he best of any roast.
His palfrey was as brown as is a berry.

The Friar

Note: Friars are also priests, but unlike cloistered monks, during this period their orders required them to go about their district begging for money. There were four religious orders of friars who lived by begging—Dominican, Franciscan, Carmelite, and Augustinian. Aside from the small amount of money necessary for them to live, they were expected to provide for the needs of the poor with the money they received. By the time of Chaucer, many friars were frequently seen as greedy, grasping men, who lined their own pockets and chased after women. While it was only suggested that the monk may have been more interested in women than a person who vows to remain celibate should have been, the friar's sexual interests are made very clear. A "limiter" was a begging friar, who was given a specific district to beg in.

A friar there was, a wanton and a merry,
A limiter, a very festive man.
In all the Orders Four is none that can
Equal his gossip and his fair language.
5   He had arranged full many a marriage

Since riding and hunting were his greatest loves, he spared no cost on them. The sleeves of his robe were decorated with the finest of gray fur, and his hood was fastened beneath his chin with a finely made gold pin that had a loveknot at the larger end. His bald head shone, and his smooth face was not creased, but was like a young man's. He was fat and he had hot, bulging eyes which he rolled about. They were red like fire. His boots were soft and his horse of great value. He was not, like some monks, as pale as some poor wasted ghost. When he sat for dinner, he loved a fat swan more than any other roast. His saddle horse was as brown as a berry.

The Friar

There was a shameless and merry friar. In all the Four Orders there was no one who could equal him in gossip and pleasant language. He had arranged many of the marriages of the young women in town and he did this at his own expense. He was a noble pillar to his Order. He knew all the wealthy landowners and women in the district and was well liked by them; when he heard their confessions, he treated them gently and gave them an easy penance, for he knew he'd get a good donation. For money given to a friar is a sure sign a man has been well confessed. He boasted that if a person gave a good donation to him, he knew that the man's repentance of his sins was genuine. For, the friar says, there are many men with hearts so hard that they cannot weep, no matter the pain; therefore instead of weeping and prayer, men should show their repentance by giving money to poor friars.

Of young women, and this at his own cost.
Unto his order he was a noble post.
Well liked by all and intimate was he
With franklins everywhere in his country,
10   And with the worthy women of the town.
He heard confession gently, it was said,
Gently absolved too, leaving naught of dread.
He was an easy man to give penance
When knowing he should gain a good pittance;
15   For to a begging friar, money given
Is sign that any man has been well shriven.
For if one gave (he dared to boast of this),
He took the man's repentance not amiss.
For many a man there is so hard of heart
20   He cannot weep however pains may smart.
Therefore, instead of weeping and of prayer,
Men should give silver to poor friars all bare.

His tippet was stuck always full of knives
And pins, to give to young and pleasing wives.
25   And certainly he kept a merry note:
Well could he sing and play upon the rote.
At balladry he bore the prize away.
His throat was white as lily of the May;
Yet strong he was as any champion.
In towns he knew the taverns, every one
30   And every good host and each barmaid too—
Better than begging lepers, these he knew.
For unto no such solid man as he
Accorded it, as far as he could see,
To have sick lepers for acquaintances.
35   There is no honest advantageousness
In dealing with such poverty-stricken curs;
It's with the rich and with big victuallers.
And so, wherever profit might arise,
Courteous he was and humble in men's eyes.
40   There was no other man so virtuous.

His hood was always stuck full with knives and pins which he gave to young, pretty wives. And he certainly kept a jolly tone. He sang and played upon a lute songs from memory so well that he had won prizes. Although he had a lily-white throat, he was as strong as any champion.

In the towns, he knew all the taverns, bartenders, and barmaids better than he knew the begging lepers. He could see no point in having sick lepers for friends, since there was no benefit to be had from dealing with these poor, contemptible creatures. It is in dealing with the rich that a profit might be gained, so wherever he might gain profit with the rich people, he was always courteous and humble. There was no other man so virtuous.

He was the finest beggar of his house;
A certain district being farmed to him,
None of his brethren dared approach its rim;
For though a widow had no shoes to show,
45   So pleasant was his *In principio*,
He always got a farthing ere he went.
He lived by pickings, it is evident.

And he could romp as well as any whelp.
For he was not like a cloisterer,
50   With threadbare cope as is the poor scholar,
But he was like a lord or like a pope.
Of double worsted was his semi-cope,
That rounded like a bell, as you may guess.
He lisped a little, out of wantonness,
55   To make his English soft upon his tongue;
And in his harping, after he had sung,
His two eyes twinkled in his head as bright
As do the stars within the frosty night.
This worthy limiter was named Hubert.

The Merchant

There was a merchant with forked beard, and girt
In motley gown, and high on horse he sat,
Upon his head a Flemish beaver hat;
His boots were fastened rather elegantly.
5   His spoke his notions out right pompously,
Stressing the times when he had won, not lost.
He would the sea were held at any cost
Across from Middleburgh to Orwell town.
At money-changing he could make a crown.
10   This worthy man kept all his wits well set;
There was no one could say he was in debt,
So well he governed all his trade affairs
With bargains and with borrowings and with shares.
Indeed, he was a worthy man withal,
15   But, sooth to say, his name I can't recall.

He was the best beggar in his order so he had an assigned district that none of the other begging friars dared to enter. When he began his speech, "In the beginning," he was so persuasive that even a poor widow without shoes gave him a donation. He got money wherever he went, and he lived well from his donations.

He could run around as well as any youngster. For he was not, like some monks, secluded in a monastery with the threadbare robe of a poor scholar. Rather he was like a lord or like a pope with his robe that went around his stomach like a bell. To make his words sound softer, he purposely lisped a little. And after he finished singing and playing the harp, his eyes twinkled as bright as any stars on a frosty night. This worthy limiter was named Hubert.

The Merchant

There was a merchant with a forked beard and a colorful gown who sat high on his horse. On his head he wore a Flemish beaver hat; his boots were fastened very elegantly and he spoke his mind very pompously when he told of his profits, but not his losses. He wanted the sea between Middleburg and Orwell to be safe for commerce at any cost. He made a profit at money changing. This worthy man kept his wits about him so well that with all his bargaining and borrowing and dealing, no one could tell that he was in debt. Indeed, he truly was a worthy man; but, to tell you the truth, I cannot recall his name.

The Clerk

A clerk from Oxford was with us also,
Who'd turned to getting knowledge, long ago.
As meagre was his horse as is a rake,
Nor he himself too fat, I'll undertake,
5   But he looked hollow and went soberly.
Right threadbare was his overcoat; for he
Had got him yet no churchly benefice,
Nor was so worldly as to gain office.
For he would rather have at his bed's head
10   Some twenty books, all bound in black and red,
Of Aristotle and his philosophy
Than rich robes, fiddle, or gay psaltery.
Yet, and for all he was philosopher,
He had but little gold within his coffer;
15   But all that he might borrow from a friend
On books and learning he would swiftly spend,
And then he'd pray right busily for the souls
Of those who gave him wherewithal for schools.
Of study took he utmost care and heed.
20   Not one word spoke he more than was his need;
And that was said in fullest reverence
And short and quick and full of high good sense.
Pregnant of moral virtue was his speech;
And gladly would he learn and gladly teach.

The Clerk

With us was a clerk from Oxford who had long since turned his mind to acquiring knowledge. The clerk's horse was as skinny as a rake, and you couldn't exactly say that he himself was fat. His coat was old and ragged because he had not yet convinced the church to support him. Nor was he wise enough in worldly ways to gain employment. He would rather have at his bedside twenty books of Aristotle's philosophy all bound in black and red, than rich robes, a fiddle, or a merry harp. Yet, for all of that he was a philosopher, who had little money saved. Any money he could borrow from friends, he quickly spent on books and learning. He busily prayed for the souls of those people who gave him the necessary money to study. He was diligent in his studies. He never spoke more than he had to; and what he did say was short, to the point, and intelligent. His speech was full of moral virtue, and he would gladly learn and teach.

The Weaver, the Dyer, and the Arras-Maker

Note: The guilds were professional organizations for craftsmen that were partly business and partly social.

An arras-maker, dyer, and weaver
Were with us, clothed in similar livery,
All of one sober, great fraternity.
Their gear was new and well adorned it was;
5   Their weapons were not cheaply trimmed with brass,
But all with silver; chastely made and well
Their girdles and their pouches too, I tell.
Each man of them appeared a proper burgess
To sit in guildhall on a high dais.
10   And each of them, for wisdom he could span,
Was fitted to have been an alderman;
For chattels they'd enough, and, too, of rent;
To which their good wives gave a free assent,
Or else for certain they had been to blame.
15   It's good to hear "Madam" before one's name,
And go to church when all the world may see,
Having one's mantle borne right royally.

The Cook

A cook they had with them, just for the nonce,
To boil the chickens with the marrow-bones,
And flavour tartly and with galingale.
Well could he tell a draught of London ale.
5   And he could roast and seethe and broil and fry,
And make a good thick soup, and bake a pie.
But very ill it was, it seemed to me,
That on his shin a deadly sore had he;
For sweet blanc-mange, he made it with the best.

The Weaver, the Dyer, and the Arras-Maker

A tapestry maker, a dyer, and a weaver were also with us, all dressed in the uniform of one great guild fraternity. Their clothes were new and fancy. Their knives were not cheaply trimmed with brass, but were trimmed in silver. Their clothes and their money bags identified them as proper citizens. Each one of them, for the wisdom that they had, deserved to be a leader of his guild. They had property that provided them a good income; for this their wives were very glad, because it is nice to have people use the word "madam." It is also nice that the world can see someone dressed like royalty in church.

The Cook

For the trip, they had a cook come with them to boil chickens with the marrow bones and to add the correct flavorings and spice. He could easily recognize a drink of the London ale, and he could roast and boil and broil and fry and make a stew as well as bake a pie. But I did not take it well that he had a festering sore on his shin. As for the sweet white meat, he made it with the best.

The Sailor

There was a sailor, living far out west;
For aught I know, he was of Dartmouth town.
He sadly rode a hackney, in a gown,
Of thick rough cloth falling to the knee.
5   A dagger hanging on a cord had he
About his neck, and under arm, and down.
The summer's heat had burned his visage brown;
And certainly he was a good fellow.
Full many a draught of wine he'd drawn, I trow,
10   Of Bordeaux vintage, while the trader slept.
Nice conscience was a thing he never kept.
If that he fought and got the upper hand,
By water he sent them home to every land.
But as for craft, to reckon well his tides,
15   His currents and the dangerous watersides,
His harbours, and his moon, his pilotage,
There was none such from Hull to far Carthage.
Hardy, and wise in all things undertaken,
By many a tempest had his beard been shaken.
20   He knew well all the havens, as they were,
From Gottland to the Cape of Finisterre,
And every creek in Brittany and Spain;
His vessel had been christened *Madeleine*.

The Sailor

There was a sailor who came from far out west. For all I know, he may have been from Dartmouth. He rode an old horse as best he could and wore a thick, coarse cloth which came down to his knees. He had a dagger hanging on a cord which went around his neck and under his arm. The hot summer had tanned his face all brown, and he was certainly a good fellow.

He had drunk many glasses of Bordeaux wine while the wine merchant slept. A good conscience was a thing he never had. If he fought and won, he sent his prisoners home by drowning them. But as for skill in judging the tides, currents, and dangerous hazards, the harbours and the moon and pilotage, there was no one like him from Hull to far Carthage. He was tough and shrewd in all his ventures and had survived many rough storms. He knew all of the safe harbors from Gottland to the Cape of Finisterre, and he knew every creek in Brittany and in Spain; his ship was named the Madeleine.

The Physician

      With us there was a doctor of physic;
      In all this world was none like him to pick
      For talk of medicine and surgery;
      For he was grounded in astronomy.
5   He often kept a patient from the pall
      By horoscopes and magic natural.
      He knew the cause of every malady,
      Were it of hot or cold, of moist or dry,
      And where engendered, and of what humour;
10   He was a very good practitioner.

      The cause being known, down to the deepest root,
      Anon he gave to the sick man his boot.
      Ready he was, with his apothecaries,
      To send him drugs and all electuaries;
15   By mutual aid much gold they'd always won—
      Their friendship was a thing not new begun.
      In diet he was measured as could be,
      Including naught of superfluity,
      But nourishing and easy. It's no libel
20   To say he read but little in the Bible.
      In blue and scarlet he went clad, withal,
      Lined with a taffeta and with sendal;
      And yet he was right chary of expense;
      He kept the gold he gained from pestilence.
25   For gold in physic is a fine cordial,
      And therefore loved the gold exceeding all.

The Physician

With us was a doctor of medicine, and in all the world there was no doctor like him to speak with of medicine or of surgery; because he had studied astrology, he often kept his patients from falling sick by the stars and some natural magic. He knew the cause of every sickness whether it was hot or cold, moist or dry, and where it came from, and which bodily fluid it affected. He was a very good practitioner.

Knowing the cause of a disease to its very root, he was ready to give the sick a remedy, and he could give an immediate remedy because he had all of his concoctions pre-mixed by a druggist. By helping each other, he and the druggist had both done very well for many years in making money from the drugs and syrups. Their friendship had not just begun. He was moderate in his diet, including nothing in excess, only that which was nourishing and simple. It is the truth to say that he did not bother to read the Bible very much. Although the cloaks he wore were done in blue and scarlet and lined with taffeta and silk, he was a frugal man. He kept the gold which he made during the plague because the gold from medicine was good for his health; therefore, above all else he loved gold.

The Wife of Bath

There was a housewife come from Bath, or near,
Who—sad to say—was deaf in either ear.
At making cloth she had so great a bent
She bettered those of Ypres and even of Ghent.
5   Her kerchiefs were of finest weave and ground;
I dare swear that they weighed a full ten pound
Which, of a Sunday, she wore on her head.
Her hose were of the choicest scarlet red,
Close gartered, and her shoes were soft and new.
10   Bold was her face, and fair, and red of hue.
She'd been respectable throughout her life,
With five churched husbands bringing joy and strife,
Not counting other company in youth;
But thereof there's no need to speak, in truth.

15   Three times she'd journeyed to Jerusalem;
And many a foreign stream she'd had to stem;
At Rome she'd been, and she'd been in Boulogne,
In Spain at Santiago, and at Cologne.
She could tell much of wandering by the way:
20   Gap-toothed was she, it is no lie to say.
Upon an ambler easily she sat,
Well wimpled, aye, and over all a hat
As broad as is a buckler or a targe,
A rug was tucked around her buttocks large,
25   And on her feet a pair of sharpened spurs.
In company well could she laugh her slurs.
The remedies of love she knew, perchance,
For of that art she'd learned the old, old dance.

The Wife of Bath

A good wife from the town of Bath was with the group, but she was somewhat deaf, and that was a pity. She had such a good knack for clothmaking, that she surpassed the clothmakers of Ypres and Ghent. In fact, her kerchiefs were so tightly woven that I would swear that the ones she wore on her head on Sunday weighed ten pounds. Her stockings were of the choicest scarlet red and pulled up tightly; her shoes were soft and new. Her face was fearless, attractive, and rosy. She had been a worthy woman all of her life, who was married five times in the church, not to mention other company in her youth, but there is no need to speak of that now, truthfully.

She had traveled to Jerusalem three times and had crossed many foreign streams. She had been to Rome and Boulogne and Santiago, Spain, and Cologne. To be sure, she knew a lot about life on the road. It is no lie to say that she was gap-toothed. She sat easily upon her walking horse with a neat veil and a hat on her head that was as wide as a small shield. A rug was tucked around her wide hips, and she wore a pair of sharp spurs on her feet. Yet she could laugh and joke with all the fellows. The many remedies on the art of love that she had learned she had acquired from her own experiences.

The Parson

There was a good man of religion, too,
A country parson, poor, I warrant you;
But rich he was in holy thought and work.
He was a learned man also, a clerk,
5   Who Christ's own gospel truly sought to preach;
Devoutly his parishioners would he teach.
Benign he was and wondrous diligent.
Patient in adverse times and well content,
As he was oft times proven; always blithe,
10   He was right loath to curse to get a tithe,
But rather would he give, in case of doubt,
Unto those poor parishioners about,
Part of his income, even of his goods.
Enough with little, coloured all his moods.

15   Wide was his parish, houses far asunder,
But never did he fail, for rain or thunder,
In sickness, or in sin, or any state,
To visit to the farthest, small and great,
Going afoot, and in his hand a stave.
20   This fine example to his flock he gave,
That first he wrought and afterwards he taught;
Out of the gospel then that text he caught,
And this figure he added thereunto—
That, if gold rust, what shall poor iron do?
25   For if the priest be foul, in whom we trust,
What wonder if a layman yield to lust?
And shame it is, if priest take thought for keep,
A shitty shepherd, shepherding clean sheep.
Well ought a priest example good to give,
30   By his own cleanness, how his flock should live.

He never let his benefice for hire,
Leaving his flock to flounder in the mire,
And ran to London, up to old Saint Paul's
To get himself a chantry there for souls,
35   But dwelt at home and kept so well the fold

The Parson

There was a good religious man with us on the trip, who was a country parson. Though he was poor, he was rich in holy thought and work. He was also a learned man, a cleric, who preached of Christ's true gospel, which he devoutly taught his parishioners. He was a kind and diligent man, who was patient in adversity, as he had proven many times. Always happy, he hated to threaten in order to get a contribution.

Rather, from his collections and from his own pocket, he would give money or goods to his poor parishioners. His attitude was that a little was enough for him.

His parish was wide with houses placed far apart, but he never neglected visiting parishioners because of rain or thunder. When sickness or trouble struck, the parson visited distant parishioners, whether they were rich or poor, on foot with a large staff in his hand. He provided a noble example to his flock because he practiced what he preached. Taking wisdom from the gospels, he added his own thoughts: If gold rusts, what will lowly iron do? For if a priest, whom we trust, is sinful, is it a wonder that an average man will sin? And other priests should note that a dirty shepherd should not watch over a clean sheep. A priest ought to set an example by his own behavior as to how his flock should live.

He never rented out his position, leaving his parishioners to struggle with problems, while he ran to St. Paul's in London to apply for a high position in the church. Rather, he stayed at home and guarded his flock well, so that no evil could make anything go wrong. This parson was a shepherd, not a mercenary. And though

That never wolf could make his plans miscarry;
He was a shepherd and not mercenary.
And holy though he was, and virtuous,
To sinners he was not impetuous,
40   Nor haughty in his speech, nor too divine,
But in all teaching prudent and benign.
To lead folk into Heaven but by stress
Of good example was his busyness.
But if some sinful one proved obstinate,
45   Be who it might, of high or low estate,
Him he reproved, and sharply, as I know.
There is nowhere a better priest, I trow.
He had no thirst for pomp or reverence,
Nor made himself a special, spiced conscience,
50   But Christ's own lore, and His apostles' twelve
He taught, but first he followed it himself.

The Plowman

With him there was a plowman, was his brother
That many a load of dung, and many another
Had scattered, for a good true toiler, he,
Living in peace and perfect charity.
5   He loved God most, and that with his whole heart
At all times, though he played or plied his art
And next, his neighbour, even as himself.
He'd thresh and dig, with never thought of pelf,
For Christ's own sake, for every poor wight
10   All without pay, if it lay in his might.
He paid his taxes, fully, fairly, well,
Both by his own toil and by stuff he'd sell.
In a tabard he rode upon a mare.

he was holy and virtuous, he did show mercy to sinners, and he was not hateful or haughty in his speech. Rather, in his teaching he was kindly and careful. It was his aim to lead people to heaven by honorable example. But if a person, whether a peasant or a noble, was stubbornly bad, he would condemn him sharply for it. A better priest, I believe, does not exist. He desired no pomp or reverence, and did not consider himself beyond reproach, but he taught the lessons of Christ and His twelve apostles and lived by them as well.

The Plowman

With this parson was his brother, a farmer, who had carted many loads of dung. He was a good and hard worker, who lived in peace and charity. He loved God the most and with all of his heart at all times, whether he prospered or suffered; and next he loved his neighbor as he loved himself. He helped his neighbor thresh and plow whenever he was capable of helping, not for the pay, but to honor God. He paid his taxes in full to his church by his own work and money from things he'd sell. In his working clothes, he rode upon a mare.

The Miller

The miller was a stout churl, be it known,
Hardy and big of brawn and big of bone;
Which was well proved, for when he went on lam
At wrestling, never failed he of the ram.
5   He was a chunky fellow, broad of build;
He'd heave a door from hinges if he willed,
Or break it through, by running, with his head.
His beard, as any sow or fox, was red,
And broad it was as if it were a spade.
10   Upon the coping of his nose he had
A wart, and thereon stood a tuft of hairs,
Red as the bristles in an old sow's ears;
His nostrils they were black and very wide.
A sword and buckler bore he by his side.
15   His mouth was like a furnace door for size.
He was a jester and could poetize,
But mostly all of sin and ribaldries.
He could steal corn and full thrice charge his fees;
And yet he had a thumb of gold, begad.
20   A white coat and blue hood he wore, this lad.
A bagpipe he could blow well, be it known,
And with that same he brought us out of town.

The Miller

The miller was a big and brawny man, which served him well when he entered wrestling contests, which he usually won. He was a powerful, well-built fellow who could pull a door from its hinges if he desired to do so, or break it in half by ramming his head into it. His beard was as red as a sow or fox, and it was as broad as a shovel. On the end of his nose he had a wart from which a tuft of hair grew; this hair was as red as the bristles in an old sow's ears; his nostrils were black and wide, and a sword and shield hung from his hip; his mouth was as large as a furnace door. He was a joker, and he could spout poetry, but most of it was about sin or other vulgar stories. With his thumb of gold which he sneaked on to the scale, he could steal corn and charge three times his usual fee. He wore a white coat and a blue hood. He could play a bagpipe well and with it, he led our group of pilgrims out of town.

The Manciple

Note: A manciple was a steward or buyer, whose job it was to buy food and supplies for a college or monastery.

There was a manciple from an inn of court,
To whom all buyers might quite well resort
To learn the art of buying food and drink;
For whether he paid cash or not, I think
5   That he so knew the markets, when to buy,
He never found himself left high and dry.
Now is it not of God a full fair grace
That such a vulgar man has wit to pace
The wisdom of a crowd of learned men?
10   Of masters had he more than three times ten,
Who were in law expert and curious;
Whereof there were a dozen in that house
Fit to be stewards of both rent and land
Of any lord in England who would stand
15   Upon his own and live in manner good,
In honour, debtless (save his head were wood),
Or live as frugally as he might desire;
These men were able to have helped a shire
In any case that ever might befall;
20   And yet this manciple outguessed them all.

The Manciple

There was a manciple for a college of lawyers, who could teach all buyers tricks when it came to buying food and drinks. For whether or not he paid cash, he knew when and where to buy so well that he always got a good price. Is it not an amazing thing that God gifted this low-born man with such a wit that he could outsmart the lawyers? Of the thirty expert and knowledgeable lawyers for whom he worked, there were twelve who were especially skilled. These twelve could have managed the land of any lord in England so he could live on his income in an honorable, debtless manner (unless his head was wood), or live as frugally as he might desire. These men would be able to help a village if the need ever befell, yet this manciple outsmarted even these twelve experts.

The Reeve

Note: A reeve served as the superintendent or manager of an estate;
he was responsible for the crops and animals.

The reeve he was a slender, choleric man,
Who shaved his beard as close as razor can.
His hair was cut round even with his ears;
His top was tonsured like a pulpiteer's.
5 Long were his legs, and they were very lean,
And like a staff, with no calf to be seen.
Well could he manage granary and bin,
No auditor could ever on him win.
He could foretell, by drought and by the rain,
10 The yielding of his seed and of his grain.
His lord's sheep and his oxen and his dairy,
His swine and horses, all his stores, his poultry,
Were wholly in this steward's managing;
And, by agreement, he'd made reckoning
15 Since his young lord of age was twenty years;
Yet no man ever found him in arrears.
There was no agent, hind, or herd who'd cheat
But he knew well his cunning and deceit;
They were afraid of him as of the death.
20 His cottage was a good one, on a heath;
By green trees shaded with this dwelling-place.

Much better than his lord could he purchase.
Right rich he was in his own private right,
Seeing he'd pleased his lord, by day or night,
25 By giving him, or lending, of his goods,
And so got thanked—but yet got coats and hoods.
In youth he'd learned a good trade, and had been
A carpenter, as fine as could be seen.
This steward sat a horse that well could trot,
30 And was all dapple-grey, and was named Scot.
A long surcoat of blue did he parade,
And at his side he bore a rusty blade.
Of Norfolk was this reeve of whom I tell,
From near a town that men call Badeswell.
35 Bundled he was like friar from chin to croup,
And ever he rode hindmost of our troop.

The Reeve

The reeve was a slender, bad-tempered man, clean-shaven as possible; his hair was cut high around his ears but clipped short in front like a priest's. His legs were long and lean and straight like a stick. He could manage a granary so well that no auditor could catch him cheating. He could predict the yield of his crops by the amount of rain or drought.

Everything on the estate had been completely under his care since the lord of the estate had been twenty years old, yet the reeve had never fallen behind in his accounts. No agent or anyone else could cheat him, because he knew all their tricks; as a result, they were deathly afraid of him. He had a good home in the countryside and it was shaded by trees.

He was a much wiser buyer than his lord; as a result, he accumulated wealth for himself as well as the lord, who was well pleased with the reeve's work. By giving or lending the lord his own goods, the reeve received thanks as well as coats and hoods. The reeve was a skilled carpenter and he rode his dapple-gray horse, called Scot, very well. He wore a long, blue coat and a rusty blade hung from his hip. The reeve was from Norfolk, which was near a town that men called Badeswell. Bundled up like a friar, the reeve rode last in the group.

The Summoner

Note: Summoners were employees of religious courts that were sent to "summon" people suspected of offenses against church law. By this period of time, however, summoners had evolved into corrupt detectives who spied on offenders and blackmailed them with the threats of summonses.

A summoner was with us in that place,
Who had a fiery-red, cherubic face,
For eczema he had; his eyes were narrow.
As hot he was, and lecherous, as a sparrow;
5 With black and scabby brows and scanty beard,
He had a face that little children feared.
There was no mercury, sulphur, or litharge,
No borax, ceruse, tartar, could discharge,
Nor ointment that could cleanse enough, or bite,

10 To free him of his boils and pimples white,
Nor of the bosses resting on his cheeks.
Well loved he garlic, onions, aye and leeks,
And drinking of strong wine as red as blood.
Then would he talk and shout as madman would.
15 And when a deal of wine he'd poured within,
Then would he utter no word save Latin.
Some phrases had he learned, say two or three,
Which he had garnered out of some decree;
No wonder, for he'd heard it all the day;
20 And all you know right well that even a jay
Can call out "Wat" as well as can the pope.
But when, for aught else, into him you'd grope,
'Twas found he'd spent his whole philosophy;
Just "Questio quid juris" would he cry.

25 He was a noble rascal, and a kind;
A better comrade 'twould be hard to find.
Why, he would suffer, for a quart of wine,
Some good fellow to have his concubine
A twelve-month, and excuse him to the full
30 (Between ourselves, though, he could pluck a gull).

The Summoner

There was a summoner with a round face that was fiery red from all the pimples he had; his eyes were narrow and lecherous.
With his scabby, black brows and scanty beard, children feared the sight of him. There was no medicine or ointment that could cure his boils and his pimple-marked face, or the lumps on his cheeks.

He loved garlic, onions, and leeks and drinking strong, red wine. When he drank, he would shout like a madman, and speak no other words but two or three Latin phrases he had learned by heart from some decree. That was no surprise because he heard these phrases all the time. He could speak them like some talking bird, who can call out "Wat" as well as the pope can; but if you asked him for anything else, he was lost, for he had exhausted all his knowledge when he called out, "By what authority?"

He was a noble and kind rascal, and better comrade would be hard to find. Why, for a quart of wine he'd let a friend take away his mistress for a year and then excuse him fully. (Between ourselves, though, he could really cheat a gullible person.)

49

The Pardoner

Note: A pardoner gave out a papal pardon, for sins, to those people who contributed to the charitable institution that he represented. A pardon could cancel out all or part of the penance imposed on sinners by their confessors.

With him there rode a gentle pardoner
Straight from the court of Rome had journeyed he.
Loudly he sang "Come hither, love, to me,"
The summoner joining with a burden round;
5   Was never horn of half so great a sound.
This pardoner had hair as yellow as wax,
But lank it hung as does a strike of flax;
In wisps hung down such locks as he'd on head,
And with them he his shoulders overspread;
10   But thin they dropped, and stringy, one by one.
But as to hood, for sport of it, he'd none,
Though it was packed in wallet all the while.
It seemed to him he went in latest style,
Dishevelled, save for cap, his head all bare.
15   His wallet lay before him in his lap,
Stuffed full of pardons brought from Rome all hot.
A voice he had that bleated like a goat.
No beard had he, nor ever should he have,
For smooth his face as he'd just had a shave;
20   I think he was a gelding or a mare.

But in his craft, from Berwick unto Ware,
Was no such pardoner in any place.
For in his bag he had a pillowcase
The which, he said, was Our True Lady's veil:
25   He said he had a piece of the very sail
That good Saint Peter had, what time he went
Upon the sea, till Jesus changed his bent.
He had a latten cross set full of stones,
And in a bottle had he some pig's bones.
30   But with these relics, when he came upon
Some simple parson, then this paragon

The Pardoner

With the summoner rode a gentle pardoner who had come straight from the court at Rome. With the summoner accompanying him, he sang loudly, "Come hither, love, to me." Never was there a trumpet half so powerful. This pardoner had hair as yellow as wax, but it hung down as smooth as a hank of flax. The wisps of hair hung down and spread over his shoulders in thin strands.

For the fun of it, he wore no hood, but kept it packed in his bag. He thought he rode in the latest style, disheveled and bareheaded except for his cap. His bag, which lay in front of him on his lap, was crammed with pardons from Rome, still warm from the oven. He had a small voice that sounded like a goat. He had no beard, nor would he ever, for his face was as smooth as if he'd just had a shave. I believe he was a gelding or a mare.

But in his occupation, from Berwick to Ware, there was no pardoner who could compete. In his bag he had a pillowcase which he said was the Virgin Mary's veil; he said he had a small piece of the sail that St. Peter had when he sailed on the sea until Jesus Christ rescued him. He had a cross of brass set full of gems, and in a glass case he had some pig's bones. With these relics, however, whenever he found a poor parson living in the country,

In that one day more money stood to gain
Than the poor dupe in two months could attain.
And thus, with flattery and suchlike japes,
35   He made the parson and the rest his apes.
But yet, to tell the whole truth at the last,
He was, in church, a fine ecclesiast.
Well could he read a lesson or a story,
But best of all he sang an offertory;
40   For well he knew that when that song was sung,
Then might he preach, and all with polished tongue,
To win some silver, as he right well could;
Therefore he sang so merrily and so loud.

Now have I told you briefly, in a clause,
45   The state, the array, the number, and the cause
Of the assembling of this company.

within a day he made more money than that parson got in two months. And so with fake sincerity and tricks, he made monkeys out of the parson and the people. But to be fair, in church he was noble; he could read a lesson or a story, and he could sing a very good oratory. For well he knew that when his song was done, then he would preach and with his sharpened tongue win silver; therefore, he sang merrily and loud.

Now, I have told you briefly the status, the dress, and the purpose of the people gathered in this company.

Comprehension Check

1. Who narrates the prologue, and what is the purpose of the prologue?

2. Why does the narrator begin by describing the knight first?

3. What do we learn of the knight's character, appearance, and history?

4. What do we learn about the squire? How is he like and unlike his father?

5. Describe the yeoman.

6. Describe the prioress. Given the fact that she is a nun, what is ironic about her brooch?

7. Keeping in mind that monks are supposed to live a cloistered life in monasteries where they devote themselves to work, prayer and study for the glory of God, what is satiric about how this monk is described?

8. What are the characteristics of the friar?

9. State what Chaucer is satirizing about Friar Hubert's features.

10. What makes the description of the clerk a positive one?

11. List and describe the three tradesmen: what is it we are told in the last three lines that their wives desire?

12. What is your initial opinion of the cook? Does your opinion change after reading the last three lines?

13. In the description of the sailor, what does Chaucer suggest through understatement?

14. What one of the physician's practices comes across most strongly?

15. Describe Dame Alice of Bath.

16. *She had been a worthy woman all of her life, who was married five times in the church, not to mention other company in her youth, but there is no need to speak of that now, truthfully.*

    What is implied about Dame Alice of Bath in the above?

17. What lines make her look like a comic figure?

18. Is the parson described in a positive or negative light? Support your opinion.

19. Is the description of the plowman positive or negative?

20. Although brief, the description of the miller is quite sharp. How do you envision his physical appearance?

21. What do we learn of the miller's personality, character, and business practices?

22. The manciple, whose job is to buy food and drink for a house of thirty lawyers, is able to cheat them. Why does the narrator act surprised?

23. Describe the summoner and state what his job in the church is.

24. What is the pardoner's job in the church? What fraud does he perpetrate?

The Nun's Priest's Prologue

"HOLD!," cried the knight. "Good sir, no more of this,
What you have said is right enough, and is
Very much more; a little heaviness
Is plenty for the most of us, I guess.
5 For me, I say it's saddening, if you please,
As to men who've enjoyed great wealth and ease,
To hear about their sudden fall, alas,
But the contrary's joy and great solace,
As when a man has been in poor estate
10 And he climbs up and waxes fortunate,
And there abides in all prosperity.
Such things are gladsome, as it seems to me,
And of such things it would be good to tell."
    "Yea, quoth our host, "and by Saint Paul's great bell,
15 You say the truth; this monk, his clapper's loud.
Sir monk, no more of this, so God you bless!
Your tale annoys the entire company;
Sir, tell a tale of hunting now, I pray."
Such things are gladsome, as it seems to me,
20 And of such things it would be good to tell."
    "Nay," said this monk, "I have no wish to play;
Now let another tell, as I have told."
    Then spoke our host out, in rude speech and bold,
And said he unto the nun's priest anon:
25 "Come near, you priest, come hither, you Sir John,
Tell us a thing to make our hearts all glad;
Be blithe, although you ride upon a jade.
What though your horse may be both foul and lean?
If he but serves you, why, don't care a bean;
30 Just see your heart is always merry. So."
    "Yes, sir," said he, "yes, host, so may I go,
For, save I'm merry, I know I'll be blamed."
And right away his story has he framed,
And thus he said unto us, every one,
35 This dainty priest, this goodly man, Sir John.

The Nun's Priest's Prologue

"Stop!" said the knight. "Good sir, no more of this. What you have said is true enough, I know, and much more; a little seriousness is quite enough for most people, I guess. Speaking for myself, it is very sad to hear of men who have had great wealth and ease, who then experience a sudden fall from their high estate. And the opposite is a great joy and comfort—when a man who has been poor climbs up and becomes fortunate and remains there in prosperity. It seems to me such things are pleasant and most fitting to talk about."

"Yes," said our host, "you speak the truth; this monk chatters loud. Sir monk, no more of this unpleasant kind of talk. Your tale annoys the entire group. Sir, instead, tell us about hunting, I beg you."

"No," said the monk, "I have no desire to entertain; now let another tell a story, because mine has been told."

Then our host spoke up, in his bold, rude way, and said to the nun's priest, straightaway, "Come near, you priest, come here; you, Sir John, tell us the sort of story that will make us happy; be merry even though your horse is a nag. So what if your horse smells and is skinny? If he carries you where you want to go, it doesn't matter; just make sure that your heart is filled with happiness."

"Yes, sir," he said. "Yes, I will proceed. I know you will be upset unless this is a happy story." He immediately began his tale, and this is what this sweet priest, this good man, Sir John, said to all of us.

The Nun's Priest's Tale
Of the Cock and Hen: Chanticleer and Pertelote

A WIDOW POOR, somewhat advanced in age,
Lived, on a time, within a small cottage
Beside a grove and standing down a dale.
This widow, now, of whom I tell my tale,
5   Since that same day when she'd been last a wife,
Had led, with patience, her strait simple life,
For she'd small goods and little income-rent;
By husbanding of such as God had sent
She kept herself and her young daughters twain.
10 Three large sows had she, and no more, 'tis pain,
Three cows and a lone sheep that she called Moll.
Right sooty was her bedroom and her hall,
Wherein she'd eaten many a slender meal.
Of sharp sauce, why she needed no great deal,
15 For dainty morsel never passed her throat;
Her diet well accorded with her coat.
Repletion never made this woman sick;
And no wine drank she,—either white or red;
Her board was mostly garnished, white and black,
20 With milk and brown bread, whereof she'd no lack,
Broiled bacon and sometimes an egg or two,
For a small dairy business did she do.
    A yard she had, enclosed all roundabout
With pales, and there was a dry ditch without,
25 And in the yard a cock called Chanticleer.
In all the land, for crowing, he'd no peer.
His voice was merrier than the organ gay
On Mass days, which in church begins to play;
More regular was his crowing in his lodge
30 Than is a clock or abbey horologe.

The Nun's Priest's Tale
Of the Cock and Hen: Chanticleer and Pertelote

A poor widow, somewhat old, once lived in a small cottage, near a grove of trees that stood in a valley. Ever since her husband had died, this widow led a very simple life. Because her property and income were small, she lived by a God-given thriftiness and thus supported herself and her two daughters. She kept three large sows, and she had three cows and one sheep named Moll.

She ate many a meager meal in her bedroom and parlor that were quite dirty. Her meals contained no spices nor added flavors, and she never ate anything fancy. Because her diet was like her thin, gray coat, she never had to worry about getting sick from overeating. She drank no wine, not red nor white; in fact, her dinner table had no color at all to it except white and black, that is white milk and brown bread, of which she had a great deal. Sometimes she had a piece of bacon or a couple of eggs from the few farm animals that she kept.

Her yard was enclosed all around with a fence made of sticks, and in that pen she kept a cock named Chanticleer. In the world of crowing, Chanticleer was the king, for his voice sounded more full than a Sunday organ. In the barn, his crowing was more accurate than a clock or the timekeeper in an abbey of monks. And when the time came to crow, he crowed so well that no other cock could crow better. His comb was redder than fine coral, and it was notched as a castle wall might be; his black bill shone as black and as polished

And when fifteen degrees had been ascended,
Then crew he so it might not be amended.
His comb was redder than a fine coral.
And battlemented like a castle wall.
35 His bill was black and just like jet it shone;
This noble cock had in his governance
Seven hens to give him pride and all pleasance,
Which were his sisters and his paramours
And wondrously like him as to colours,
40 Whereof the fairest hued upon her throat
Was called the winsome Mistress Pertelote.
Courteous she was, discreet and debonnaire,
Companionable, and she had been so fair
That truly she had taken the heart to hold
45 Of Chanticleer, he locked on her every limb;
He loved her so that all was well with him.
But such a joy it was to hear them sing,
Whenever the bright sun began to spring,
In sweet accord, "My love walks through the land."
50   So it befell that, in a bright dawning,
As Chanticleer 'midst wives and sisters all
Sat on his perch, the which was in the hall,
And next him sat the winsome Pertelote,
This Chanticleer he groaned within his throat
55 Like man that in his dreams is troubled sore.
And when fair Pertelote thus heard him roar,
She was aghast and said: "O sweetheart dear,
What ails you that you groan so? Do you hear?
You are a sleepy herald. Fie, for shame!"
60   And he replied to her thus: "Ah, madame,
I pray you that you take it not in grief,
By God. I dreamed I'd come to such mischief,
Just now, my heart yet jumps with sore affright.
I dreamed, that while I wandered up and down
65 Within our yard, I saw there a strange beast
Was like a dog, and he'd have made a feast
Upon my body, and have had me dead.
His snout was small and gleaming was each eye.
Remembering how he looked, almost I die;
70 And all this caused my groaning, I confess."

as coal. Under his protection, this noble cock had seven hens, wives and sisters all, who had colors as wonderful as his. The fairest of them all was named fair Miss Pertelote. She was courteous, discrete and carefree, and she made Chanticleer a good wife.

Chanticleer fell in love with her every limb, and loved her so much that all was well with him. When the bright sun began to rise, it was beautiful to hear them sing together. In sweet harmony they would sing, "My love steps through the land."

So it happened that one morning Chanticleer sat sleeping on his perch among all of his wives. A groan started in his throat that was like the sound of a person having a bad dream. When Pertelote heard him groan, she was shocked and said, "Oh dear, what is it that makes you groan this way? You are half asleep; this is embarrassing."

He answered, "Madam, I hope that you don't take this too hard, but by God, I dreamed I was in bad trouble. I do admit that just now my heart was really frightened. I dreamed that as I roamed up and down inside our yard, I saw a beast. This beast was like a hound who wanted to grab me and would have killed and eaten me. He had a small snout and two glowing eyes. He looked so terrible that I am still close to death just in remembering it. I confess that this was what caused my groaning."

"Aha," said she, "fie on you, spiritless!
Alas!" cried she, "for by that God above,
Now have you lost my heart and all my love;
I cannot love a coward, by my faith.
75   For truly, whatsoever woman saith,
We all desire, if only it may be,
To have a husband hardy, wise, and free.
How dare you say, for shame, unto your love
That there is anything that you have feared?
80   Have you not man's heart, and yet have a beard?
Alas! And are you frightened by a vision?
Dreams are, God knows, a matter for derision.
Visions are generated by repletions
And vapours and the body's bad secretions."
85   "Lo, Cato, and he was a full wise man,
Said he not, we should trouble not for dreams?
Now, sir," said she, "when we fly from the beams,
For God's love go and take some laxative;
On peril of my soul, and as I live,
90   I counsel you the best, I will not lie.
Be merry, husband, for your father's kin!
Dread no more dreams. And I can say no more."
    "Madam," said he, "gramercy for your lore.
Nevertheless, not running Cato down,
95   Who had for wisdom such a high renown,
And though he says to hold no dreams in dread,
By God, men have, in many old books, read
Of many a man more an authority
Who say just the reverse of his sentence,
100   And have found out by long experience
That dreams, indeed, are good significations,
As much of joys as of all tribulations
That folk endure here in this life present.
There is no need to make an argument;
105   The very proof of this is shown indeed."
    "One of the greatest authors that men read
Says thus: That on a time two comrades went
On pilgrimage, and all in good intent;
And it so chanced they came into a town

"Shame on you!" she said. "You lack spirit! By God, I swear that now you have lost my heart and my love, for I cannot love a coward. For no matter what a woman says, we all want a husband to be brave, wise, and generous. How dare you embarrass us and say to me that anything can make you afraid? Have you a man's beard but not his heart? Alas, and are you afraid of a dream? There is nothing in a dream except nonsense. Dreams come from eating too much, getting gas, and other digestive problems."

"Consider Cato, that wise man; has he not said that we should pay no attention to dreams? Now sir," said she, "when we fly down from our perch, for the love of God take a laxative. I am giving you some good advice and I mean it. You are your father's son, so don't be afraid of a dream; I cannot say any more."

"Madam," he said, "thank you for your advice. But regarding Cato, even though he advised not to be afraid of dreams, many other wise writers have said exactly the opposite. These wise men have had experiences that make them think that dreams do tell the future of joys as well as sorrows that folks here must endure. There is no point in arguing about this, since the proof is plainly seen.

"A story by one of our greatest authors tells us that once two friends went on a pilgrimage; it so happened that they came to a town where there was such a crowd that there was no place to stay. So, the two were forced to leave each other for the night and each

110   Where there was such a crowding, up and down
Of people, and so little harbourage,
That they found not so much as one cottage
Wherein the two of them might sheltered be.
Wherefore they must, as of necessity,

115   For that one night at least, part company;
And each went to a different hostelry
And took such lodgment as to him did fall.
Now one of them was lodged within a stall,
Far in a yard, with oxen of the plow;

120   That other man found shelter fair enow,
As was his luck, or was his good fortune,
Whatever 'tis that governs us, each one."
    "So it befell that, long ere it was day,
This last man dreamed in bed, as there he lay,

125   That his poor fellow did unto him call,
Saying: 'Alas! For in an ox's stall
This night shall I be murdered where I lie.
Now help me, brother dear, before I die.
Come in all haste to me. 'Twas that he said.

130   This man woke out of sleep, then, all afraid;
But when he'd wakened fully from his sleep,
He turned upon his pillow, yawning deep,
Thinking his dream was but a fantasy.
And then again, while sleeping, thus dreamed he.

135   And then a third time came a voice that said
(Or so he thought): 'Now, comrade, I am dead;
Behold my bloody wounds, so wide and deep!
Early arise tomorrow from your sleep,
And at the west gate of the town,' said he,

140   'A wagon full of dung there shall you see,
Wherein is hid my body craftily;
Do you arrest this wagon right boldly.
They killed me for what money they could gain.'
And told in every point how he'd been slain,

145   With a most pitiful face and pale of hue.
And trust me well, this dream did all come true;
For on the morrow, soon as it was day,
Unto his comrade's inn he took the way;

find on his own some place to sleep. While one of them was forced to sleep in a stall for oxen, in a barn far from the center of town, the other man was lucky to find a nice bed at an inn. It was just the luck or fortune that governs all of us the same.

"So it happened that shortly after falling asleep, the man in the bed had a dream that his friend was calling him. 'Alas!' said his friend, 'I am in an ox's stall, and will be murdered tonight while I sleep. Now help me, dear brother, before I die. Come in all haste to me.'

"The man, frightened out of his sleep, woke up; but he then rolled over and paid no more attention to the dream, for he thought the dream was only fantasy. Again this happened, and again the man went back to sleep.

"The third time the friend's voice came in a dream, the apparition said, 'Now, comrade, I am dead; look at my bloody wounds! Get up early tomorrow morning and near the west gate of town you will find a cart full of manure. Hidden in the bottom of the cart will be my body. You must boldly stop this wagon, for they have killed me and have taken all my money.' And with a pale, pitiful face he related all the details of the crime. Trust me, Pertelote, all the events in this dream did come true. For early the next morning, the friend went to the inn at which his comrade had stayed, and at the ox's stall he called out his friend's name.

And when he'd come into that ox's stall
150 Upon his fellow he began to call."
     "The keeper of the place replied anon,
And said he: 'Sir, your friend is up and gone;
As soon as day broke he went out of town.'
This man, then, felt suspicion in him grown,
155 Remembering the dream that he had had,
And forth he went, no longer tarrying, sad,
Unto the west gate-of the town, and found
A dung-cart on its way to dumping-ground,
And it was just the same in every wise
160 As you have heard the dead man advertise;
And with a hardy heart he then did cry
Vengeance and justice on this felony:
'My comrade has been murdered in the night,
And in this very cart lies, face upright.
165 I cry to all the officers,' said he
'That ought to keep the peace in this city.
Alas, alas, here lies my comrade slain!'"
     "Why should I longer with this tale detain?
The people rose and turned the cart to ground,
170 And in the center of the dung they found
The dead man, lately murdered in his sleep."
     "O Blessed God, Who art so true and deep!
Lo, how Thou dost turn murder out alway!
Murder will out, we see it every day.
175 Murder's so hateful and abominable
To God, Who is so just and reasonable,
That He'll not suffer that it hidden be;
Though it may skulk a year, or two, or three,
Murder will out, and I conclude thereon.
180 Immediately the rulers of that town,
They took the carter and so sore they racked
Him and the host, until their bones were cracked,
That they confessed their wickedness anon,
And hanged they both were by the neck, and soon.
185 And therefore, pretty Pertelote, my dear,
By such an old example may you hear
And learn that no man should be too reckless

"At which, the keeper of the place replied: 'Sir, your friend is already up and gone.' The man, growing quite suspicious and remembering his dream, quickly went to the west gate of town. There he found a dung cart, setting out to go fertilize the land, just as his dream had described. With a bold heart, he cried out for revenge and justice for this crime. 'My friend was murdered last night, and he lies dead in this cart.' He said, 'I cry out to peace officers in this city that here lies my slain friend.'

"With this the people gathered around and overturned the cart and in the pile of dung they found the body of the man who had just been murdered.

"O Blessed God, Who is so true, we see every day that you find murder so hateful that you will not tolerate a murder to be hidden.

"Though a murder may be hidden for a year or two, or three, eventually it will be exposed. And on that point I will conclude. Immediately, the authorities cracked the bones of the cart driver and the innkeeper until they confessed their crime. Both were quickly hanged by the neck.

"And therefore, my lady Pertelote, by this example you should learn that nobody should be too thoughtless when it comes to

Of dreams, for I can tell you, fair mistress,
That many a dream is something well to dread.
190 Upon this point I say, concluding here,
That from this vision I have cause to fear
Adversity; and I say, furthermore,
That I do set by laxatives no store,
For they are poisonous, I know it well.
195 Them I defy and love not, truth to tell."
 "But let us speak of mirth and stop all this;
For when I see the beauty of your face,
You are so rosy-red beneath each eye,
It makes my dreadful terror wholly die.
200 For when I feel at night your tender side,
I am so full of joy and all solace
That I defy, then, vision, aye and dream."
And with that word he flew down from the beam,
For it was day, and down went his hens all;
205 And with a cluck he them began to call,
For he had found some corn within the yard.
Regal he was, and fears he did discard.
He looked as if he were a grim lion
As on his toes he strutted up-and-down;
210 He deigned not set his foot upon the ground.
He clucked when any grain of corn he found,
And all his wives came running at his call.
Thus regal, as prince is in his hall,
I'll now leave busy Chanticleer to feed,
215 And with events that followed I'll proceed.
 Since March began, full thirty days and two,
It fell that Chanticleer, in all his pride,
His seven wives a-walking by his side,
Cast up his two eyes toward the great bright sun.
220 "The sun, my love," he said, "has climbed anew.
My lady Pertelote, whom I adore,
Mark now these happy birds, hear how they sing.
And see all these fresh flowers, how they spring;
Full is my heart of revelry and grace."
225 But suddenly he fell in grievous case;
For ever the latter end of joy is woe.

dreams for there are many dreams that should be feared. In concluding here, I have cause to fear this dream, and furthermore, I do not think laxatives do any good, and I don't like them.

"But let us speak of joyful things and stop all this. For when I see the beauty of your face, you are so rosy red around your eyes that all my fear is gone away. When I feel your soft side at night, I am so full of joy and comfort that I ignore any other vision or dream." With that he flew down from his roost and all of his hens did the same. After finding some corn on the ground, he called them with a cluck. He was regal again and no longer afraid; he strutted around like a fierce lion and he pranced and clucked whenever he found a grain of corn, and all his wives came running at his call. Thus, as royal as any prince in his castle, I'll now leave Chanticleer to his dinner, and tell you of that which followed.

It happened one March morning that Chanticleer, in all his pride, was walking with his seven wives when he looked up at the bright sun. "Lady Pertelote," he said, "my world is bliss; listen to the birds and look at the flowers in full bloom; my heart is full of joy and satisfaction."

But suddenly, serious trouble arose, for the end of every joy is sorrow. God knows that worldly joys swiftly leave. But now I must take up my proper theme.

God knows that wordly joys do swiftly go.
But now I must take up my proper theme.
   A brant-fox, full of sly iniquity,
230 That in the grove had lived two years, or three,
Now by a fine premeditated plot
That same night, breaking through the hedge, had got
Into the yard where Chanticleer the fair
Was wont, and all his wives too, to repair;
235 And in a bed of greenery still he lay
Till it was past the quarter of the day,
Waiting his chance on Chanticleer to fall.
O Chanticleer, accursed be that morrow
When you into that yard flew from the beams!
240 You were well warned, and fully, by your dreams
That this day should hold peril damnably.
But that which God foreknows, it needs must be.
Whether the fact of God's great foreknowing
Makes it right needful that I do a thing
245 (By needful, I mean, of necessity);
Or else, if a free choice he granted me,
To do that same thing, or to do it not,
Though God foreknew before the thing was wrought;
Or if His knowing constrains never at all,
250 Save by necessity conditional.
I have no part in matters so austere;
My tale is of a cock, as you shall hear,
That took the counsel of his wife, with sorrow,
Now women's counsels oft are ill to hold;
255 A woman's counsel brought us first to woe,
And Adam caused from Paradise to go,
Wherein he was right merry and at ease.
But since I know not whom it may displease
If woman's counsel I hold up to blame,
260 Pass over, I but said it in my game.
Read authors where such matters do appear,
And what they say of women, you may hear.
These are the cock's words, they are none of mine;
No harm in women can I e'er divine.
265   All in the sand, a-bathing merrily,

A sly, black fox, who lived nearby, had broken through the fence that night and had gotten into the yard where Chanticleer and his wives browsed. This fox lay hidden in a bed of vegetables until well into the afternoon, all the while waiting to pounce on Chanticleer. O, Chanticleer, that morning was cursed once you left your safe perch and flew into the yard.

You had been thoroughly warned by your dreams that this day would be dangerous; but that which God foreknows must be. But if God foreknows what I will do, does it follow that I'll do it, or did he grant me free will to choose to do it, or not do it? I have no part in deciding such heavy questions. My story is about a cock, who, sadly, took the advice of his wife, and women's advice is often dangerous. It was a woman's advice that made Adam leave a paradise where he had been perfectly happy and relaxed. But since I don't know who I might annoy if I go on being critical of the advice of women, let me just say to forget this part; I was only kidding.

Read other writers who specialize in this type of thing, and you can learn what they say about women. Anyway, this is the cock speaking, not me. I see no harm in women.

Lay Pertelote, with all her sisters by,
There in the sun; and Chanticleer so free
Sang merrier than mermaid in the sea
(For Physiologus says certainly
270   That they do sing, both well and merrily).
And so befell that, as he cast his eye
Among the herbs and on a butterfly,
He saw this fox that lay there, crouching low.
Nothing of urge was in him, then, to crow;
275   But he cried "Cock-cock-cock" and did so start
As man who has a sudden fear at heart.
For naturally a beast desires to flee
From any enemy that he may see.
    He would have fled but that the fox anon
280   Said: "Gentle sir, alas! Why be thus gone?
Are you afraid of me, who am your friend?
Now surely, I were worse than any fiend
If I should do you harm or villainy.
I came not here upon your deeds to spy;
285   But, certainly, the cause of my coming
Was only just to listen to you sing.
For truly, you have quite as fine a voice
As angels have that Heaven's choirs rejoice.
Save you, I never heard a man so sing
290   As did your father in the grey dawning;
Truly 'twas from the heart, his every song.
And that his voice might ever be more strong,
He took such pains that, with his either eye
He had to blink, so loudly would he cry,
295   A-standing on his tiptoes therewithal,
Stretching his neck till it grew long and small.
And such discretion, too, by him was shown,
There was no man in any region known
That him in song or wisdom could surpass.
300   I have well read, in *Dan Burnell the Ass*,
Among his verses, how there was a cock,
Because a priest's son gave to him a knock
Upon the leg, while young and not yet wise,
He caused the boy to lose his benefice.
305   But, truly, there is no comparison

Meanwhile, Lady Pertolote and the other hens were basking in the sun as Chanticleer strutted about singing as happily as a mermaid. (For Physiologus says that they sing, both well and merrily). And so it happened that as he glanced at a butterfly that was flying above the vegetables, he noticed the fox crouched down in the vegetable patch. With nothing like an urge to crow, the best he could do was begin, "Cock, cock!" like a man frightened to his heart. This, did instinct do to him, for to run away from a natural enemy is one's first thought.

He would have fled, but the fox quickly said, "Gentle sir, wait! Where are you going? Are you afraid of me, your friend? I surely would be worse than a fiend if I should do you harm. I did not come to spy on you. The cause of my coming was to hear you sing, for you have as fine a voice as angels that sing in a heavenly choir.

"Except for you, I have never heard anyone sing as well as your father did at dawn. Everything he sang came from his heart. And to make his voice stronger, he would concentrate so much that he would close both his eyes, stand up on his tip toes, and stretch his neck way up. And truly there was none in any region who could sing as well as he, or was as wise as he. I have read in the poem Dan Burnell the Ass, about a cock who caused a priest's son to lose his health because the boy had broken the cock's leg, but there is no comparison here with your father's wisdom. Now be generous and sing, dear sir, and let us see if you can imitate your father."

With the great wisdom and the discretion
Your father had, or with his subtlety.
Now sing, dear sir, for holy charity,
See if you can your father counterfeit."
310   This Chanticleer his wings began to beat,
As one that could no treason there espy,
So was he ravished by this flattery.
Alas, you lords! Full many a flatterer
Is in your courts, and many a cozener,
315   That please your honours much more, by my fay,
Than he that truth and justice dares to say.
Go read the Ecclesiast on flattery;
Beware, my lords, of all their treachery!
      This Chanticleer stood high upon his toes,
320   Stretching his neck, and both his eyes did close,
And so did crow right loudly, for the nonce;
And Russel Fox, he started up at once,
And by the gorget grabbed our Chanticleer,
Flung him on back, and toward the wood did steer,
325   For there was no man who as yet pursued.
O destiny, you cannot be eschewed!
Alas, that Chanticleer flew from the beams!
Alas, his wife recked nothing of his dreams!
      This simple widow and her daughters two
330   Heard these hens cry and make so great ado,
And out of doors they started on the run
And saw the fox into the grove just gone,
Bearing in his mouth the cock away.
And then they cried, "Alas, and weladay!
335   Oh, the fox!" and after him they ran,
And after them, with staves, went many a man;
Ran Coll, our dog, ran Garland,
Ran cow and calf and even the very hogs,
So were they scared by barking of the dogs
340   And shouting men and women all did make,
They all ran so they thought their hearts would break.
      And now, good men, I pray you hearken all.
Behold how Fortune turns all suddenly
The hope and pride of even her enemy!
345   This cock, which now lay in the fox's mouth,

74

Chanticleer, so overtaken by the flattery, began to beat his wings. He was like a person who cannot see danger. Take note all you lords; there are many flatterers and hypocrites in your courts who please you more than the people who tell you the truth. Go read the Bible about flattery; you should beware of these kinds of people.

With this, Chanticleer stood high on his toes, and stretching his neck and keeping his eyes closed, he began to crow loudly. And Sir Russell, the fox, immediately jumping up and grabbing Chanticleer by the throat, carried him into the woods. O, destiny, you cannot be avoided. Alas, that Chanticleer ever flew down from his perch! Alas, that his wife cared not about his dreams!

Meanwhile, the simple widow and her two daughters, hearing the hens crying and flapping about, quickly ran outside just in time to see the fox heading into the grove with Chanticleer in his mouth. They cried out, "Help! Stop! Stop that fox!" and after him they ran. And after them ran men brandishing sticks; and a cow, a calf, even some hogs that were scared by the shouting men and women and the barking dogs, joined the chase. They all ran so fast, they thought their hearts would quit.

Now good men, I ask you to listen to how fortune suddenly turns against the hope and pride of even her enemy. The cock, even though he was deathly afraid, said to the fox: "Sir, if I were you, I

In all his fear unto the fox did clack
And say: "Sir, were I you, as I should be,
Then would I say (as God may now help me!),
'Turn back again, presumptuous peasants all!
350   A very pestilence upon you fall!
Now that I've gained here to this dark wood's side,
In spite of you this cock shall here abide.
I'll eat him, by my faith, and that anon!'"
    The fox replied: "In faith, it shall be done!"
355   And as he spoke that word, all suddenly
This cock broke from his mouth, full cleverly,
And high upon a tree he flew anon.
And when the fox saw well that he was gone,
"Alas," quoth he, "O Chanticleer, alas!
360   I have against you done a base trespass
In that I frightened you, my dear old pard,
When you I seized and brought from out that yard;
But, sir, I did it with no foul intent;
Come down, and I will tell you what I meant.
365   I'll tell the truth to you, God help me so!
    "Nay then," said he, "beshrew us both, you know,
But first, beshrew myself, both blood and bones,
If you beguile me, having done so once,
You shall no more, with any flattery,
370   Cause me to sing and closeup either eye;
For he who shuts his eyes when he should see,
And wilfully, God let him ne'er be free!"
    "Nay," said the fox, "but God give him mischance
Who is so indiscreet in goverance
375   He chatters when he ought to hold his peace."
    But you that hold this tale a foolery,
As but about a fox, a cock, a hen,
Yet do not miss the moral, my good men.
For Saint Paul says that all that's written well
380   Is written down some useful truth to tell.
Then take the wheat and let the chaff lie still.
    And now, good God, and if it be Thy will,
As says Lord Christ, so make us all good men
And bring us into His high bliss. Amen.

would turn back, and shout at these peasants, 'turn back, all you fools. Now that I've gained the dark side of the woods, despite your efforts, the cock will stay here with me until I eat him!'"

The fox replied, "By my faith, it will be done." And as he spoke these words, the cock broke from his mouth and flew up high into a tree. When the fox saw that Chanticleer was gone, he said, "Alas, O, Chanticleer, I have done you a wrong in that I frightened you when I seized and carried you from the yard. But, sir, I did not have an evil intent. Come down and I will explain my purpose. So help me God, I'll tell you true."

"Oh no," Chanticleer said. "I curse the two of us. I curse myself more though, if I let you trick me more than once. You shall not again, with your flattery, get me to sing with my eyes closed. For God will not let a person be free who willfully blinks when he should be looking."

"No," said the fox, "but God will give the man misfortune, who is so lacking in self control that he goes on talking when he ought to hold his peace."

But, good men, those of you who consider this but a foolish tale about a fox, a cock, and a hen, do not miss the moral. For St. Paul says that which is written well has some useful truths to tell. Then take the serious meaning and leave the rest.

And now if it be God's will, Lord make us all good men and bring us into His high bliss. Amen.

Comprehension Check

The Nun's Priest's Tale

1. The first half-page describes the farm on which Chanticleer lives, and the widow who owns the farm. What is noteworthy about the widow's life?

2. In what way does Chanticleer's life and character contrast with the widow's?

3. Why do you suppose this tale may be seen as a parody of courtly love?

4. Explain what the tale's narrator, the nun's priest, says about free will.

5. In what way does the nun's priest link Chanticleer's dire situation with man's loss of paradise?

6. Why do you suppose the priest said that his critical comment about women was only a joke?

7. What is the obvious moral the narrator expects his listeners to draw from this tale?

8. What piece of learning does the fox pass on to the listeners?

The Knight's Tale

Roman Gods Alluded to in This Tale

Venus - The Roman goddess of love is depicted as a beautiful woman and accompanied by her son the cherub, Cupid.

Mars - The Roman god of war is depicted as a powerful, red warrior and a wrathful figure.

Diana - The Roman goddess of the forest and the hunt is depicted as a woman carrying a bow.

Saturn - The Roman god of agriculture is presented in this story as an older and wiser god, who is able to devise strategies to please everyone.

Mercury - The Roman god of commerce and travel is portrayed as showing compassion and giving assistance to Arcita.

Figures from Greek Mythology

Theseus - The Duke of Athens is a firm but fair ruler who shows both wisdom and humanity. Among his exploits he had conquered the land of the Amazons and wed their queen, Hippolyta. He is a strong conqueror but capable of tempering justice with mercy. He represents the social order and is its upholder.

Hippolyta - The former Queen of the Amazons, is now happily married to Theseus. As the story opens, she is on her way to Athens to live with her husband. She is accompanied by her beautiful sister Emily, who, like the other Amazons, is generally more interested in hunting than in men and/or romance.

Creon is ruler of Thebes. Creon and Thebes have just been defeated in battle by Theseus and Athens. Among the dead bodies, two cousins are found alive. These cousins, **Palamon** and **Arcita**, are part of Creon's royal family.

80

Concepts Familiar to Chaucer's Readers

The Code of Courtly Love: In the literature of the Middle Ages, there were conventions regarding a knight's love for a noble woman. The gallant and courageous knight always had to adore and respect the beautiful, intelligent and lofty minded noblewoman, who usually remained chaste and unattainable. While he performs noble deeds for her sake, he suffers terribly because she remains indifferent to him. If not indifferent, she does not grant him any sexual favors, and because of her purity and his respect for it, they never consummate their love. In addition, because she is married he must keep her name secret. The lady will, however, give the knight some token like a glove or scarf, to carry into battle with him. While he suffers a great deal because of this love, he sings of his love and his suffering. He welcomes the suffering because it inspires him to greater achievements.

Divine Providence was a popular idea in the Middle Ages. As the name implies, it holds that man's fate or fortune in life was ordained by God from the time the man was born. Although man had free will and could make choices, whatever was to occur would.

Note: Like many of Chaucer's and Shakespeare's stories, the general plot line of most of these tales was well known to Chaucer's readers, but the delight was in the way the story was retold.

The Knight's Tale is a rather simple story about friendship and courtly love. It is an interesting narrative told in verse with many good images. When reading the verse, be careful to read from punctuation mark to punctuation mark. It may be helpful, even when reading alone, to read it aloud. That could help you fall in with the cadence. The more you read in verse, the easier it is to follow.

The Knight's Tale

ONCE ON A TIME, as old tales tell to us,
There was a duke whose name was Theseus;
Of Athens he was lord and governor,
And in his time was such a conqueror
5   That greater was there not beneath the sun.
Full many a rich country had he won;
What with his wisdom and his chivalry
He gained the realm of Femininity,
That was of old time known as Scythia.
10 There wedded he the queen, Hippolyta,
And brought her home with him to his country.
In glory great and with great pageanty,
And, too, her younger sister, Emily.
And thus, in victory and with melody,
15 Let I this noble duke to Athens ride.
With all his armed host marching at his side.

    This duke of whom I speak, of great renown,
When he had drawn almost unto the town,
In all well-being and in utmost pride,
20 He grew aware, casting his eyes aside,
That right upon the road, as suppliants do,
A company of ladies, two by two,
Knelt, all in black, before his cavalcade;
But such a clamorous cry of woe they made
25 That in the whole world living man had heard
No such a lamentation, on my word;
Nor would they cease lamenting till at last
They'd clutched his bridle reins and held them fast.
    "What folk are you that at my home-coming
30 Disturb my triumph with this dolorous thing?"
Cried Theseus. "Do you so much envy

The Knight's Tale

Once upon a time, as old tales tell us, there was a duke by the name of Theseus, who was a great lord and governor of Athens. In his time, there was not a greater conqueror in the whole world. He had conquered many rich countries, and with his wisdom and his knights, he conquered the land of the Amazons, which was in olden times known as Scythia. In Scythia, he wedded its queen, Hippolyta, and with great pomp and pageantry he brought her and her younger sister Emily home with him to his own country. And so, in victory and with song, I let this noble duke ride to Athens with all his army marching at his side.

When this great duke in all his glory and pride drew close to town, he looked around and became aware that on the road in front of his procession, kneeling in the bowed positions of those who seek favors, was a group of ladies, two by two, dressed all in black. They made such a loud cry of sorrow that, I swear, living man had never heard such expressions of grief. These women would not stop crying until they had snatched Theseus' bridle reins and held them tightly.

"What folks are you that disturb my triumphant homecoming with all this crying?" cried Theseus. "Do you envy my fame so much that it causes you to complain and cry like this? Or has someone

My honour that you thus complain and cry?
Or who has wronged you now, or who offended?
Come, tell me whether it may be amended;
35   And tell me, why are you clothed thus in black?"
     The eldest lady of them answered back,
After she'd swooned, with cheek so deathly drear
That it was pitiful to see and hear,
And said: "Lord, to whom Fortune has but given
40   Victory, and to conquer where you've striven,
Your glory and your honour grieve not us;
But we beseech your aid and pity thus.
Have mercy on our woe and our distress.
Some drop of pity, of your gentleness,
45   Upon us wretched women, oh, let fall!
For see, lord, there is no one of us all
That has not been a duchess or a queen;
Now we are captives, as may well be seen:
Thanks be to Fortune and her treacherous wheel,
50   There's none can rest assured of constant weal.
And truly, lord, expecting your return,
In Pity's temple, where the fires yet burn.
We have been waiting through a long fortnight;
Now help us, lord, since it is in your might."
55   "I, wretched woman, who am weeping thus,
Was once the wife of King Capaneus,
Who died at Thebes, oh, cursed be the day!
And all we that you see in this array,
And make this lamentation to be known,
60   All we have lost our husbands at that town
During the siege that round about it lay.
And now the old Creon, ah welaway!
The lord and governor of Thebes city,
Full of his wrath and all iniquity,
65   He, in despite and out of tyranny,
To do the dead a shame and villainy,
Of all our husbands, lying among the slain,
Has piled the bodies in a heap, amain,
And will not suffer them, nor give consent,
70   To buried be, or burned, nor will relent,
But sets his dogs to eat them, out of spite."

84

wronged or offended you? If so, tell me if I can fix the situation; and tell me, why are all of you dressed in black?"

The eldest lady in the group answered back, after she had fainted, with a face so deathly sad that it was pitiful to see and hear; she said: "Lord Theseus, to whom Fortune has given victory in all of your battles, the glory and honor you achieved does not sadden us. But we beg for your help and compassion. Have mercy on our sorrow and distress. Oh please let some drops of pity fall, some gentleness, upon us wretched women. For you see, lord, there is not one of us present who has not been a duchess or a queen. Now, as you can see, we are all captives of misfortune; thanks to Fortune and her treacherous ways, none of us can be certain of our own future welfare. And truly, lord, we've awaited your presence these long two weeks in the temple where we prayed for your return. Now, help us, lord, since it is in your power to do so.

"I, this wretched woman who is weeping so, was once the wife of King Capaneus, who was killed at Thebes. Oh, cursed be that day! All of us that you see in this group, who cry out to you, have lost our husbands in the battle that took place at that town. And now Creon, lord and governor of Thebes, filled with anger and evil, and out of spite and a desire to shame the dead, has piled the dead bodies of our slain husbands in a heap. And he will not permit us to give them a proper burial or cremation. Instead, out of spite, he sets his dogs loose to eat them."

And on that word, at once, without respite,
They all fell prone and cried out piteously:
"Have on us wretched women some mercy,
75   And let our sorrows sink into your heart!
        This gentle duke down from his horse did start
With heart of pity, when he'd heard them speak.
It seemed to him his heart must surely break,
And in his arms he took them tenderly,
80   Giving them comfort understandingly:
And swore his oath, that as he was true knight,
He would put forth so thoroughly his might
Against the tyrant Creon as to wreak
Vengeance so great that all of Greece should speak
85   And say how Creon was by Theseus served,
As one that had his death full well deserved.
This sworn and done, he no more there abode;
His banner he displayed and forth he rode
Toward Thebes, and all his host marched on beside.
90   Thus rode this duke, thus rode this conqueror,
And in his host of chivalry the flower,
Until he came to Thebes and did alight
Full in the field where he'd intent to fight.
But to be brief in telling of this thing,
95   With Creon, who was Thebes' dread lord and king,
He fought and slew him, manfully, like knight,
In open war, and put his host to flight;
And by assault he took the city then,
Levelling wall and rafter with his men;
100   And to the ladies he restored again
The bones of their poor husbands who were slain,
To do for them the last rites of that day.
        In searching through the heap of enemy dead,
Stripping them of their gear from heel to head,
105   The busy pillagers could pick and choose,
After the battle, what they best could use;
And so befell that in a heap they found,
Pierced through with many a grievous, bloody wound,
Two young knights lying together, side by side,
110   And of those two Arcita was the one,

And suddenly without pausing, they all fell prone and cried out piteously: "Have mercy on us wretched women and let our sorrows sink into your heart!"

Hearing this story, the gentle duke came down from his horse with a heart full of pity. It seemed to him that his heart would surely break; and he took the women in his arms tenderly and comforted them with understanding. And he swore his oath as a true knight that he would put all of his strength into defeating the tyrant Creon and inflict vengeance so great that all of Greece would speak and say that Theseus gave Creon the kind of death which he deserved. This sworn and done, he remained there no longer; he raised his flag and rode forth toward Thebes, and all of his army marched with him.

Thus rode Duke Theseus, thus rode this conqueror, and in his army the finest knights, until he came to Thebes. There he dismounted his horse in the field where he intended to fight. But to be brief in telling this story, there Theseus fought Creon, who was Thebes' dread lord and king. Manfully, like a knight in open war, Theseus fought and slew Creon and drove his army away; and by attacking, he and his men then took the city, knocking down the walls and roofs. And to the ladies he restored the bones of their poor slain husbands, so that they might give them a proper burial and last rites on that day.

In searching through the heap of the enemy dead after the battle and stripping them of their gear, the busy looters could pick and choose what they could best use. And so it happened that in a heap they found two young knights pierced through with many a grievous, bloody wound lying together, side by side. And of those two one was Arcita; the other knight was known as Palamon. They were not fully alive, yet not fully dead. But by their coats of arms and by their gear, Theseus' soldiers could tell that they were of the Theban

The other knight was known as Palamon.
Not fully quick, nor fully dead they were,
But by their coats of arms and by their gear
The heralds readily could tell, withal,
115 That they were of the Theban blood royal,
And that they had been of two sisters born.
Out of the heap the spoilers had them torn
And carried gently over to the tent
Of Theseus; who shortly had thern sent
120 To Athens, there in prison cell to lie
For ever, without ransom till they die.
And when this worthy duke had all this done,
He gathered host and home he rode anon,
With laurel crowned again as conqueror;
125 There lived he in all joy and all honour
His term of life; what more need words express?
And in a tower, in anguish and distress,
Palamon and Arcita, day and night,
Dwelt whence no gold might help them to take flight.
130   Thus passed by year by year and day by day,
Till it fell out, upon a morn in May,
That Emily, far fairer to be seen
Than is the lily on its stalk of green,
And fresher than is May with flowers new
135 (For with the rose's colour strove her hue,
I know not which was fairer of the two),
Before the dawn, as was her wont to do,
She rose and dressed her body for delight;
For May will have no sluggards of the night.
140 That season rouses every gende heart
And forces it from winter's sleep to start,
Saying: "Arise and show thy reverence."
So Emily remembered to go thence
In honour of the May, and so she rose.
145 Clothed, she was sweeter than any flower that blows;
Her yellow hair was braided in one tress
Behind her back, a full yard long, I guess.
And in the garden, as the sun up-rose,
She sauntered back and forth and through each close,

blood royal, and that they were cousins. They were taken from the heap and carried gently over to the tent of Theseus, who had them sent to Athens; there they were to be imprisoned forever in a cell until they died without any hope of ever being ransomed. And when this worthy duke had done all, he gathered his army and rode home crowned with laurel again as conqueror; there he lived in all joy and all honor for the rest of his life; what more needs to be said?

And imprisoned in a tower, in anguish and distress, Palamon and Arcita lived day and night in a place from which no gold might help them escape.

Thus passed year by year and day by day until one morning in May when Emily, far lovelier than the lily on its stalk of green and fresher than May with its new flowers, rose and dressed before the dawn as was her custom, for May will not tolerate lazy people of the night. That season rouses every gentle heart and forces it to wake up from winter's sleep saying, "Arise and show thy respect." So Emily remembered to go therefore in honor of May, and so she rose. Dressed, she was sweeter than any flower that blooms. Her yellow hair was tied in one braid behind her back, a full yard long, I guess. And in the garden, as the sun rose, she strolled back and forth through each pathway, gathering many red and white flowers so that she might weave a delicate garland for her head. And like a heavenly angel's was her singing.

150   Gathering many a flower, white and red,
       To weave a delicate garland for her head;
       And like a heavenly angel's was her song.
          The tower tall, which was so thick and strong,
       And of the castle was the great donjon,
155   (Wherein the two knights languished in prison,
       Of whom I told and shall yet tell, withal),
       Was joined, at base, unto the garden wall
       Whereunder Emily went dallying.
       Bright was the sun and clear that morn in spring,
160   And Palamon, the woeful prisoner,
       As was his wont, by leave of his gaoler
       Was up and pacing round that chamber high,
       From which the noble city filled his eye,
       And, too, the garden full of branches green,
165   Wherein bright Emily, fair and serene
       Went walking and went roving up and down.
       This sorrowing prisoner, this Palamon,
       Being in the chamber, pacing to and fro,
       And to himself complaining of his woe,
170   Cursing his birth, he often cried "Alas!"
       And so it was, by chance or other pass,
       That through a window, closed by many a bar
       Of iron, strong and square as any spar,
       He cast his eyes upon Emilia,
175   And thereupon he blenched and cried out "Ah!"
       As if he had been smitten to the heart.
          And at that cry Arcita did up-start,
       Asking: "My cousin, why what ails you now
       That you've so deathly pallor on your brow?
180   Why did you cry out? Who's offended you?
       For God's love, show some patience, as I do,
       With prison, for it may not different be;
       Fortune has given this adversity.
       Some evil disposition or aspect
185   Of Saturn did our horoscopes affect
       To bring us here, though differently 'twere sworn;
       But so the stars stood when we two were born;
       We must endure it; that, in brief, is plain."

The tall tower, which was so thick and strong, was the great dungeon of the castle (where the two knights whose story I tell languished in prison) and was joined at its base to the wall of the garden where Emily strolled. The sun was bright and clear that spring morning, and Palamon, the wretched prisoner, with permission from his jailer, was as usual walking around that high chamber from which he could see the noble city and the garden full of green branches where bright Emily, fair and peaceful, went walking and roaming up and down. This suffering prisoner, this Palamon, in the chamber pacing to and fro and complaining to himself of his misery, cursing his birth, often cried "Alas!" And so it was by chance that through a window strongly barred with iron he first saw Emily; and at that moment he turned pale and cried out "Ah!" as if he had been pierced in the heart.

And at that cry Arcita did look up and ask, "My cousin, why what ails you now that you've become so deathly pale? Why did you cry out? Who has offended you? For God's love, show some patience, as I do with prison, because it can't be any different; Fortune has given us this adversity. Some evil disposition or aspect of Saturn affected our horoscopes to bring us to this; but the stars decided our fate when we two were born, so we must endure it; that, in short, is clear."

This Palamon replied and said again:
190 "It's not our prison that caused me to cry.
But I was wounded lately through the eye
Down to my heart, and that my bane will be.
The beauty of the lady that I see
There in that garden, pacing to and fro,
195 Is cause of all my crying and my woe.
I know not if she's woman or goddess;
But Venus she is verily, I guess."
And thereupon down on his knees he fell,
And said: "O Venus, if it be thy will
200 To be transfigured in this garden, thus
Before me, sorrowing wretch, oh now help us
Out of this prison to be soon escaped.
And if it be my destiny is shaped,
By fate, to die in durance, in bondage,
205 Have pity, then upon our lineage
That has been brought so low by tyranny."
    And on that word Arcita looked to see
This lady who went roving to and fro.
And in that look her beauty struck him so
210 That, if poor Palamon is wounded sore,
Arcita is as deeply hurt, and more.
And with a sigh he said then, piteously:
"The virgin beauty slays me suddenly
Of her that wanders yonder in that place;
215 And save I have her pity and her grace,
That I at least may see her day by day,
I am but dead; there is no more to say."
    This Palamon, when these words he had heard,
Pitilessly he watched him, and answered:
220 "Do you say this in earnest or in play?"
    "Nay," quoth Arcita, "earnest, now, I say!
God help me, I am in no mood for play!
    Palamon knit his brows and stood at bay.
"It will not prove," he said, "to your honour
225 After so long a time to turn traitor
To me, who am your cousin and your brother.
Sworn as we are, and each unto the other,

Palamon replied and said, "It's not our prison that caused me to cry. I was wounded through the eye down to my heart, and that will be my misfortune. The beauty of the lady that I see pacing to and fro in the garden is cause of all my crying and my woe. I don't know if she's woman or goddess; but she is truly Venus, I guess." Falling on his knees, he said: "O Venus, if it be your will to be transformed in this garden before this sorrowing wretch, now help us to escape from this prison. And if it is my destiny to die in bondage, have pity, then, upon our family who has been brought so low by tyranny."

Hearing all this, Arcita looked to see this lady who was walking back and forth. And in that look Emily's beauty struck Arcita so, that if poor Palamon is wounded painfully, Arcita is as deeply hurt, and more.

With a sigh Arcita then said piteously: "The pure beauty of her who wanders yonder in that place unexpectedly overwhelms me. Unless I win her pity and her favor so I may at least see her day by day, I am dead; there is no more to say."

When Palamon heard these words he looked at Arcita without feeling and asked, "Do you say this in earnest or in play?"

"No," said Arcita, "I am serious! God help me, I am in no mood for play!"

Palamon frowned and stood back. "It will not be to your honor," he said, "after so long a time to turn traitor on me who is your cousin and your brother. We have sworn to protect and care for each other and to let nothing come between us till death shall part us. Nor shall either of us get in the way of the other in love or in

That never, though for death in any pain,
Never, indeed, till death shall part us twain,
230   Either of us in love shall hinder other,
No, nor in any thing, O my dear brother;
But that, instead you shall so further me
As I shall you. All this we did agree.
Such was your oath and such was mine also.
235   You dare not now deny it, well I know.
And now you would all falsely go about
To love my lady, whom I love and serve,
And shall while life my heart's blood may preserve.
Nay, false Arcita, it shall not be so.
240   I loved her first, and told you all my woe,
As to a brother and to one that swore
To further me, as I have said before.
For which you are in duty bound, as knight,
To help me, if the thing lie in your might,
245   Or else you're false, I say, and downfallen"
     Then this Arcita proudly spoke again:
"You shall," he said, "be rather false than I;
And that you're so, I tell you utterly;
For *par amour* I loved her first, you know.
250   What can you say? You know not, even now,
Whether she is a woman or goddess!
Yours is a worship as of holiness,
While mine is love, as of a mortal maid;
Wherefore I told you of it, unafraid,
255   As to my cousin and my brother sworn.
Let us assume you loved her first, this morn;
Know you not well the ancient writer's saw
Of 'Who shall give a lover any law?'
Love is a greater law, aye by my pan,
260   Than man has ever given to earthly man.
And therefore statute law and such decrees
Are broken daily and in all degrees.
A man must needs have love, maugre his head.
He cannot flee it though he should be dead,
265   And be she maid, or widow, or a wife.
And yet it is not likely that, in life,

anything else, O, my dear brother. Instead, we agreed that I will help you and you will help me. Such was your oath and mine also. You don't dare deny it now, I know. And now you would be disloyal to love my lady, whom I love and serve, and shall as long as I live. No, disloyal Arcita, it shall not be so. I loved her first and told you of my sorrow as to a brother who swore to help me, as I have said before. You are duty bound as a knight to help me if it is within your power. Otherwise you are a liar, I say, and ruined."

Then Arcita proudly spoke again: "You shall," he said, "be more disloyal than I; and you are, I tell you absolutely. As for love, I loved her first, you know. What can you say? You do not know, even now, whether she is a woman or a goddess! Your love is like holy worship, while mine is love for a mortal maid; wherefore I told you of my love, unafraid, as to my sworn cousin and brother. Let us assume you loved her first this morning; don't you know well the ancient writer's saying, 'Who shall give a lover any law?' Love is a greater law, by my mind, than man has ever given to man. And, therefore, legal laws and decrees are broken daily to various degrees.

A man must have love in spite of what his mind tells him. He cannot run away from it even though it kills him. But, yet, whether she is a maiden, a widow, or a wife, it is not likely that in life, either of us shall ever win her. You are well aware that you and I

You'll stand within her graces; nor shall I;
For you are well aware, aye verily,
That you and I are doomed to prison drear
270   Perpetually; we gain no ransom here.
We strive but as those dogs did for the bone
They fought all day, and yet their gain was none.
Till came a kite while they were still so wroth
And bore the bone away between them both.
275   And therefore, at the king's court, O my brother,
It's each man for himself and not for other.
Love if you like; for I love and aye shall;
And certainly, dear brother, that is all.
Here in this prison cell must we remain
280   And each endure whatever fate ordain."
      Great was the strife, and long, betwixt the two,
If I had but the time to tell it you,
Save in effect. It happened on a day
(To tell the tale as briefly as I may),
285   A worthy duke men called Pirithous,
Who had been friend unto Duke Theseus,
Since each had been a little child, a chit,
Was come to visit Athens and visit
His play-fellow, as he was wont to do,
290   For in this whole world he loved no man so;
And Theseus loved him as truly—nay,
So well each loved the other, old books say,
That when one died (it is but truth I tell),
The other went and sought him down in Hell,
295   But of that tale I have no wish to write.
Pirithous loved Arcita, too, that knight,
Having known him in Thebes full many a year;
And finally, at his request and prayer,
And that without a coin of ransom paid,
300   Duke Theseus released him out of shade,
Freely to go where'er he wished, and to
His own devices, as I'll now tell you.
      The compact was, to set it plainly down,
That if Arcita, any time, were found,
305   Ever in life, by day or night, on ground

are doomed to this dreary prison forever; we get no ransom here. We struggle like two dogs who fought over a bone all day, but got nothing out of it, until a hawk came along while they were still so angry and carried the bone away right between them both. And therefore, O my brother, at the king's court it's each man for himself and not for the other. Go ahead and love her if you like; for I will do the same. And certainly, dear brother, that is all. We must remain here in this prison cell and each endure whatever fate has decided."

Great and lengthy was the struggle between the two, but I have not time to tell it all; one day (to tell the story as briefly as I can), a worthy duke called Pirithous, who had been a friend of Duke Theseus since they were children, came to visit Athens and visit his friend as he was accustomed to doing, for in this whole world he loved no man so well; and Theseus loved him just as much. Pirithous and Theseus loved each other so much that, as the old books tell, when one died (I only relate the truth), the other went to Hell to seek him out. But I have no wish to write about that story. Pirithous also loved Arcita, having known that knight for many years in Thebes.

Finally, at Pirithous's earnest request, and without any ransom paid, Duke Theseus released Arcita out of darkness to go freely wherever he wished and to do as he wished, as I will now tell you.

The agreement was, to state it clearly, that if Arcita were ever found on any of Theseus' land and caught, he would immediately have his head chopped off. He had no choice, so he left

Of any country of this Theseus,
And he were caught, it was concerted thus,
That by the sword he straight should lose his head.
He had no choice, so taking leave he sped
310 Homeward to Thebes, lest by the sword's sharp edge
He forfeit life. His neck was under pledge.
    How great is Arcita's sorrow now!
How through his heart he feels death's heavy blow;
He weeps, he wails, he cries out piteously;
315 He thinks that he may slay himself all privily.
Said he: "Alas, the day that I was born!
I'm in worse prison, now, and more forlorn;
Now am I doomed eternally to dwell
No more in Purgatory, but in Hell.
320 Alas, that I have known Pirithous!
For else had I remained with Theseus,
Fettered within that cell; but even so
Then had I been in bliss and not in woe.
Only the sight of her that I would serve,
325 Though I might never her dear grace deserve,
Would have sufficed, oh well enough for me!
O my dear cousin Palamon," said he,
"Yours is the victory, and that is sure,
For there, full happily, you may endure.
330 In prison? Never, but in Paradise!
Oh, well has Fortune turned for you the dice,
Who have the sight of her, I the absence.
For possible it is, in her presence,
You being a knight, a worthy and able,
335 That by some chance, since Fortune's changeable,
You may to your desire sometime attain.
But I, that am in exile and in pain,
Stripped of all hope and in so deep despair
That there's no earth nor water, fire nor air,
340 Nor any creature made of them there is
To help or give me comfort, now, in this—
Surely I'll die of sorrow and distress;
Farewell, my life, my love, my joyousness!"

and sped homeward to Thebes for fear that he would lose his life by the sword's sharp edge. His life depended on his keeping the agreement.

Very great is Arcita's sorrow now! In his heart he feels death's heavy blow; he weeps, he wails, he cries out piteously; he thinks about killing himself. Said he: "Curse the day I was born! I'm in a worse prison now, and more miserable. I am doomed eternally to dwell not in Purgatory, but in Hell. Alas, that I have known Pirithous! Otherwise, I would have remained with Theseus chained within that cell; but even so, then I had been in bliss and not in woe. Just the sight of her that I would serve, even though I might never deserve her dear favor, would have sufficed to make me happy!

"O my dear cousin Palamon," said he, "Yours is the victory, and that is sure, for there you live happily; you endure. In prison? Never, but in Paradise! Oh, Fortune has turned the dice in your favor, for you have the sight of her, I the absence. It is possible since Fortune is changeable that you, being a worthy and able knight and there in her presence, might by some chance attain your desire. But I, in exile and in pain, stripped of all hope and in deep despair because there's no earth nor water, fire nor air, nor any creature made of them able to help or give me comfort in this. Surely I'll die of sorrow and distress; farewell, my life, my love, my joyousness!

"Alas! Why is it men complain so much of what God, or Fortune, may determine when that may be a better gift than anything men may devise for themselves. One man desires great wealth, which may cause his death, or a life filled with ill health. Someone who would gladly be free from prison might be slain by his own servants at home."

"Alas! Why is it men so much complain
345 Of what great God, or Fortune, may ordain,
When better is the gift, in any guise,
Than men may often for themselves devise?
One man desires only that great wealth
Which may but cause his death or long ill-health.
350 One who from prison gladly would be free,
At home by his own servants slain might be."
And on the other hand, this Palamon,
When that he found Arcita truly gone,
Such lamentation made he, that the tower
355 Resounded of his crying, hour by hour.
The very fetters on his legs were yet
Again with all his bitter salt tears wet.
"Alas!" said he, "Arcita, cousin mine,
With all our strife, God knows, you've won the wine.
360 You're walking, now, in Theban streets, at large,
And all my woe you may from mind discharge.
You may, too, since you've wisdom and manhood,
Assemble all the people of our blood
And wage a war so sharp on this city
365 That by some fortune, or by some treaty,
You shall yet have that lady to your wife
For whom I now must needs lay down my life.
For surely 'tis in possibility,
Since you are now at large, from prison free,
370 And are a lord, great is your advantage
Above my own, who die here in a cage.
For I must weep and wail, the while I live,
In all the grief that prison cell may give,
And now with pain that love gives me, also,
375 Which doubles all my torment and my woe."
Now will I leave this Palamon, for he
Is in his prison, where he still must dwell,
And of Arcita will I forthwith tell.
Summer being passed away and nights grown long,
380 Increased now doubly all the anguish strong
Both of the lover and the prisoner.
I know not which one was the woefuller.
For, to be brief about it, Palamon

On the other hand, when Palamon found out that Arcita was truly gone he grieved so much that the tower resounded with his crying, hour after hour. The chains on his legs were wet with all his bitter tears. "Alas!" said Palamon. "Arcita, my cousin, after all our troubles, God knows, you have won the wine. You are now walking freely in Theban streets and you may forget about all my misery. And since you have wisdom and courage, you may assemble all the people of our blood and wage a war so severe on this city that by some fortune or treaty you shall yet have that lady to be your wife for whom I would lay down my life. It is truly a possibility since you are now free from prison and are a lord that your advantage is greater than mine, which dies here in a cage. For while I live, I must weep and wail with all the grief that a prison cell may cause. And also, now with pain that love causes me, which doubles all my torment and my sorrow."

Now I will leave this Palamon, for he is in his prison where he still must dwell, and I will now tell of Arcita. Summer passed and the nights grew long, which doubly increased the intense anguish of both the lover and the prisoner. I do not know which one was the worse off. For, to be brief about it, Palamon is doomed to lie forever in chains and shackles in prison until he is dead; and exiled (on the loss of his head) Arcita must remain abroad and nevermore see the face of the lady he loves.

Is doomed to lie for ever in prison,
385   In chains and fetters till he shall be dead;
And exiled (on the forfeit of his head)
Arcita must remain abroad, nor see,
For evermore, the face of his lady.
     You lovers, now I ask you this question:
390   Who has the worse, Arcita or Palamon?
The one may see his lady day by day,
But yet in prison must he dwell for aye.
The other, where he wishes, he may go,
But never see his lady more, ah no.
395   Now answer as you wish, all you that can,
For I will speak right on as I began.
     Now when Arcita unto Thebes was come,
He lay and languished all day in his home,
Since he his lady nevermore should see,
400   But telling of his sorrow brief I'll be.
Had never any man so much torture,
No, nor shall have while this world may endure.
Bereft he was of sleep and meat and drink,
That lean he grew and dry as shaft, I think.
405   His eyes were hollow and ghasty to behold,
His face was sallow, all pale and ashen-cold,
And solitary kept he and alone,
Wailing the whole night long, making his moan.
And so changed was he, that no man could know
410   Him by his words or voice, whoever heard.
And in this change, for all the world he fared
As if not troubled by malady of love,
But by that humor dark and grim, whereof
Springs melancholy madness in the brain,
415   And fantasy unbridled holds its reign.
And shortly, all was turned quite upside-down,
Both habits and the temper all had known
Of him, this woeful lover, Dan Arcita.
     Upon a night, while sleeping in his bed,
420   He dreamed of how the winged God Mercury,
Before him stood and bade him happier be.
His sleep-bestowing wand he bore upright;

You lovers, I ask you this question: Who has it the worst, Arcita or Palamon? The one may see his lady day by day but must dwell in prison forever. The other may go where he wishes but never again see his lady. Now answer as you wish, all you that can, for I will continue as I began.

When Arcita came to Thebes, he lay about in his home all day and suffered with longing because he would never see his lady again, but in telling of his sorrow I'll be brief. Never had any man so much torture, no, nor will have while this world may endure. He so deprived himself of sleep and food and drink that he grew thin and dry as an old shaft, I think. His eyes were hollow and ghastly to behold, his face was all pale and ashen-cold, and he kept to himself, avoiding all company. He cried and moaned the whole night long, and if he heard a song or instrument, then he would weep uncontrollably. So low and feeble were his spirits and so changed was he, that no man who heard him would recognize him by his words or voice. And in this change, people thought that he was troubled not by a malady of love, but by a dark and grim humor from which comes a melancholy madness in the brain and the rule of unrestrained fantasy. And shortly, everything was turned quite upside-down, both the habits and temper everyone had known belonged to this sorrowful lover, Dan Arcita.

One night, while sleeping in his bed, he dreamed that the winged God Mercury stood before him and told him to be happier. He held his sleep-bestowing wand upright and wore a hat upon his bright ringlets. This god was dressed as he had been when he gave sleep

103

A hat he wore upon his ringlets bright.
Arrayed this god was (noted at a leap)
425 As he'd been when to Argus he gave sleep.
And thus he spoke: "To Athens shall you wend;
For all your woe is destined there to end."
And on that word Arcita woke and started.
"Now truly, howsoever sore I'm smarted,"
430 Said he, "to Athens right now will I fare;
Nor for the dread of death will I now spare
To see my lady, whom I love and serve;
I will not reck of death, with her, nor swerve."
And with that word he caught a great mirror,
435 And saw how changed was all his old colour,
And saw his visage altered from its kind.
And right away it ran into his mind
That since his face was now disfigured so,
By suffering endured (as well we know),
440 He might, if he should bear him low in town,
Live there in Athens evermore, unknown,
Seeing his lady well-nigh every day.
And right anon he altered his array,
Like a poor labourer in mean attire,
445 And all alone, save only for a squire,
Who knew his secret heart and all his case,
And who was dressed as poorly as he was,
To Athens was he gone the nearest way.
And to the court he went upon a day,
450 And at the gate he proffered services
To drudge and drag, as any one devises.
And to be brief herein, and to be plain,
He found employment with a chamberlain
Who was serving in the house of Emily;
455 For he was sharp and very soon could see
What every servant did who served her there.
Right well could he hew wood and water bear,
For he was young and mighty, let me own,
And big of muscle, aye and big of bone,
460 To do what any man asked in a trice.
A year or two he was in this service,

to Argus. And thus he spoke: "To Athens you shall go, and all your woe is destined to end there." And on that word Arcita awoke and jumped up. "Now truly, however badly I'm grieving," he said, "to Athens right now I will go; not for the fear of death will I give up seeing my lady whom I love and serve; I will not be concerned about death, nor let it distract me."

And with that word he got a mirror and saw how his old color had changed and saw his appearance altered from its original. And right away he realized that since his face was now so disfigured from the suffering he had endured (as we well know), he might, if he should carry himself as a lowly person in town, live there in Athens forever, unrecognized, seeing his lady almost every day. And he immediately changed his fine clothes to dress like a poor laborer in shabby attire. And with only his squire who knew his secret heart and his whole story and was dressed as poorly as he was, he went to Athens the shortest way. He went to the palace one day and at the gate he offered his services as a porter or laborer.

And to be brief and frank, he found employment with the chamberlain of Emily's house. Since he was so smart, he soon learned what every servant who worked there did. Because he was young and strong with large muscles and bones, he could hew wood and carry water well and do what any man asked him to do in a very short time. For a year or two he was in this service as page of the chamber of Emily the beautiful. He said "Philostrates" was his name. But there was never a man in his position at that palace who was loved half so well as he. His gentle nature was so clearly shown that his reputation spread throughout the palace. People said that it

Page of the chamber of Emily the bright;
He said "Philostrates" would name him right.
But half so well beloved a man as he
465   Was never in that court, of his degree;
His gentle nature was so clearly shown,
That throughout all the court spread his renown.
They said it were but kindly courtesy
If Theseus should heighten his degree
470   And put him in more honourable service
Wherein he might his virtue exercise.
And thus, anon, his name was so up-sprung,
Both for his deeds and sayings of his tongue,
That Theseus had brought him nigh and nigher
475   And of the chamber he had made him squire,
And given him gold to maintain dignity.
Besides, men brought him, from his own country,
From year to year, clandestinely, his rent;
But honestly and slyly it was spent,
480   And no man wondered how he came by it.
And three years thus he lived, with much profit,
And bore him so in peace and so in war
There was no man that Theseus loved more.
And in such bliss I leave Arcita now,
485   And upon Palamon some words bestow.
     In darksome, horrible, and strong prison
These seven years has now sat Palamon,
Wasted by woe and by his long distress.
Who has a two-fold heaviness
490   But Palamon? whom love yet tortures so
That half of his wits he is for woe;
And joined thereto he is a prisoner,
Perpetually, not only for a year.
And who could rhyme in English, properly,
495   His martyrdom? Forsooth, it is not I;
And therefore I pass lightly on my way.
     It fell out in the seventh year, in May,
On the third night (as say the books of old
Which have this story much more fully told),
500   Were it by chance or were it destiny

would be a kindly compliment if Theseus should give him a better position and put him in a more honorable service where he might better exercise his virtue.

And thus, because people spoke so well of him both for his actions and his words, Theseus promoted him to squire of the palace and gave him gold to maintain his position. In addition, men from his own country secretly paid for his rent each year; but it was spent so honestly and cleverly that no man wondered where it came from. He lived for three years with much profit, and bore himself so well in peace and in war that there was no man that Theseus loved more. And in this bliss I leave Arcita now, and of Palamon some words I now will speak.

Palamon has now sat in the dark, horrible, and strong prison these seven years, wasted by sorrow and his long suffering. Who has a double burden except Palamon? He, whom love tortures so that he is half out of his wits for woe; and in addition to that, he is a prisoner, not only for a year, but forever. And who could properly rhyme in English, his martyrdom? In truth, it is not I; and therefore I pass lightly on my way.

It happened on the third night in May of the seventh year (as say the old books, which tell these stories in more detail) either by chance or destiny (since when a thing is destined, it must be), that shortly after midnight Palamon, with the help of a friend, escaped

107

(Since, when a thing is destined, it must be),
That, shortly after midnight, Palamon,
By helping of a friend, broke from prison,
And fled the city, fast as he might go;
505 For he had given his guard a drink that so
Was mixed of spice and honey and certain wine
And Theban opiate and anodyne,
That all that night, although a man might shake
This gaoler, he slept on, nor could awake.
510 And thus he flees as fast as ever he may.
  The night was short and it was nearly day,
Wherefore he needs must find a place to hide;
And to a grove that grew hard by, with stride
Of furtive foot, went fearful Palamon.
515 In brief, he'd formed his plan, as he went on,
That in the grove he would lie fast all day,
And when night came, then would he take his way
Toward Thebes, and there find friends, and of them pray
Their help on Theseus in war's array;
520 And briefly either he would lose his life,
Or else win Emily to be his wife;
This is the gist of his intention plain.
  Now I'll return to Arcita again,
Who little knew how near to him was care
525 Till Fortune caught him in her tangling snare.
The busy lark, the herald of the day,
Salutes now in her song the morning grey;
And fiery Phoebus rises up so bright
That all the east is laughing with the light,
530 And with his streamers dries, among the greves,
The silver droplets hanging on the leaves.
And so Arcita, in the court royal
With Theseus, and his squire principal,
Is risen, and looks on the merry day.
535 And now, to do his reverence to May,
Calling to mind the point of his desire,
He on a courser, leaping high like fire,
Is ridden to the fields to muse and play,
Out of the court, a mile or two away;

from prison and fled the city as fast as he could. He had given his guard a drink that mixed a spice, honey, and wine with Theban opiate and a painkiller; as a result all that night the jailer slept and could not be awakened, even if a man shook him. Thus, Palamon ran away as fast as possible.

The night was short and it was nearly dawn, so Palamon had to find a place to hide. Fearful Palamon went with a stealthy stride into a nearby grove of trees. He quickly formed his plan as he went: he would lie still in the grove all during the day, then rise and flee at night towards Thebes, and there find friends and beg their help to wage war on Theseus; shortly he would either lose his life or win Emily for his wife. This is the gist of his plan.

Now I'll return to Arcita, who had little idea that danger was so near, until Fortune caught him in her tangling trap. The busy lark, who introduces the day, now salutes the gray morning with her song; and fiery Phoebus rises so bright that all the East laughs with the light, and his rays dry the dewdrops hanging on the leaves. And so Arcita, in the royal palace with Theseus and as his principal squire, rises and looks out on the merry day. And now, to honor May and thinking of Emily, he rides his spirited horse out of the palace a mile or two away to the fields to daydream and play. By accident, his way began to lead to the grove I recently mentioned to make himself the garland one weaves of woodbine leaves and green hawthorn leaves. And he sang loudly in the bright sunlight: "Oh May, with all thy flowers and all thy green, you are welcome, thou fair and freshening May: I hope to pick some green garland today."

540 And to the grove, whereof I lately told,
By accident his way began to hold,
To make him there the garland that one weaves
Of woodbine leaves and of green hawthorn leaves.
And loud he sang within the sunlit sheen:
545 "O May, with all thy flowers and all thy green,
Welcome be thou, thou fair and freshening May:
I hope to pluck some garland green today."
And on a path he wandered up and down,
Near which, and as it chanced, this Palamon
550 Lay in the thicket, where no man might see,
For sore afraid of finding death was he.
He knew not that Arcita was so near:
God knows he would have doubted eye and ear,
But it has been a truth these many years
555 That "Fields have eyes and every wood has ears."
It's well for one to bear himself with poise;
For every day unlooked-for chance annoys.
And little knew Arcita of his friend,
Who was so near and heard him to the end,
560 Where in the bush he sat now, keeping still.
    Arcita, having roamed and roved his fill,
and having sung, began to speak,
And sat him down, sighing like one forlorn.
"Alas," said he, "the day that I was born!
565 How long, O Juno, of thy cruelty,
Wilt thou wage bitter war on Thebes city?
Alas! Confounded beyond all reason
The blood of Cadmus and of Amphion;
Of royal Cadmus, who was the first man
570 To build at Thebes, and first the town began,
And first of all the city to be king;
Of his lineage am I, and his offspring,
By true descent, and of the stock royal:
And now I'm such a wretched serving thrall,
575 That he who is my mortal enemy,
I serve him as his squire, and all humbly.
And even more does Juno give me shame,
For I dare not acknowledge my own name;

He wandered up and down on a path near which, by chance, Palamon lay in the thicket where no man might see him because he was so afraid of dying. He did not know that Arcita was so near; God knows he would have doubted his eyes and ears. But it has been a truth for many years that "Fields have eyes and every forest has ears." It's important for one to carry himself with composure because every day unexpected coincidence is bothersome. Arcita didn't realize that he was so near to his friend, who was hiding quietly in the bushes, and heard everything he said.

After having sung and roamed about at his pleasure, Arcita sat down, sighing like one forlorn and began to speak. "Alas," he said, "the day that I was born! How long, O Juno, with your cruelty will you wage bitter war on Thebes city? It is not to be believed that I, the heir to the throne of Cadmus and Amphion, the son of Cadmus, the founder and first King of Thebes, and of royal blood, am now a lowly servant to a man who is my mortal enemy. I serve him as a humble squire, but Juno heaps even more shame on me because I dare not reveal my true name. Whereas Arcita was my rightful name, now I'm Philostrates which is worth nothing.

But whereas I was Arcita by right,
580 Now I'm Philostrates, not worth a mite.
Alas, thou cruel Mars! Alas, Juno!
Thus have your angers all our kin brought low,
Save only me, and wretched Palamon,
Whom Theseus martyrs yonder in prison.
585 And above all, to slay me utterly,
Love has his fiery dart so burningly
Struck through my faithful and care-laden heart,
My death was patterned ere my swaddling-shirt.
You slay me with your two eyes, Emily;
590 You are the cause for which I now must die.
For on the whole of all my other care
I would not set the value of a tare,
So I could do one thing to your pleasance!"
And with that word he fell down in a trance
595 That lasted long; and then he did up-start.
　　This Palamon, who thought that through his heart
He felt a cold and sudden sword blade glide,
For rage he shook, no longer would he hide.
But after he had heard Arcita's tale,
600 As he were mad, with face gone deathly pale,
He started up and sprang out of the thicket,
Crying: "Arcita, oh you traitor wicked,
Now are you caught, that crave my lady so,
For whom I suffer all this pain and woe,
605 And have befooled the great Duke Theseus,
And falsely changed your name and station thus:
Either I shall be dead or you shall die.
You shall not love my lady Emily,
But I will love her, and none other, no;
610 For I am Palamon, your mortal foe.
And though I have no weapon in this place,
Being but out of prison by God's grace,
I say again, that either you shall die
Or else forgo your love for Emily.
615 Choose which you will, for you shall not depart."
　　This Arcita, with scornful, angry heart,
When he knew him and all the tale had heard,

"Alas, cruel Mars! Alas, Juno! Your angers have brought down our family, except for me and miserable Palamon whom Theseus tortures in that prison. And now, to finish me completely, love has struck his fiery dart so burningly through my faithful and care-laden heart, and my death was destined before I was ever born. You slay me with your two eyes, Emily; you are the cause for which I now must die. For all my other troubles, I am not concerned at all, if I could do but one thing for you!" And with that word he fell down in a long trance; and then he jumped up.

Palamon, feeling as though his heart had been pierced with a sudden, cold sword blade, shook with rage and would no longer hide. After he had heard Arcita's tale, he jumped up and sprang out of the thicket as if he were crazy, with face gone deathly pale, cry-ing: "Arcita, oh you wicked traitor. Now you are caught; you who wish to steal my lady for whom I suffer all this pain and sorrow, and you who have deceived the great Duke Theseus and falsely changed your name and station. Either I shall be dead or you shall die. You shall not love my lady Emily, for I will love her and none other; for I am Palamon, your mortal foe. And though I have no weapon here, just having escaped from prison by God's grace, I say again that either you shall die or else give up your love for Emily. Choose which you will, for you shall not leave."

When Arcita saw Palamon and heard all he had to say, Arcita, with scornful, angry heart and fierce as a lion, pulled a sword and

113

Fierce as a lion, out he pulled a sword
And answered thus: "By God that sits above!
620 Were it not you are sick and mad for love,
And that you have no weapon in this place,
Out of this grove you'd never move a pace,
But meet your death right now, and at my hand.
For I renounce the bond and its demand
625 Which you assert that I have made with you.
What, arrant fool, love's free to choose and do,
And I will have her, spite of all your might!
But in as much as you're a worthy knight
And willing to defend your love, in mail,
630 Hear now this word: tomorrow I'll not fail
(Without the cognizance of any wight)
To come here armed and harnessed as a knight,
And to bring arms for you, too, as you'll see;
And choose the better and leave the worse for me.
635 And meat and drink this very night I'll bring,
Enough for you, and clothes for your bedding.
And if it be that you my lady win
And slay me in this wood that now I'm in,
Then may you have your lady, for all of me."
640   This Palamon replied: "I do agree."
And thus they parted till the morrow morn,
When each had pledged his honour to return.
    Arcita rode into the town anon,
And on the morrow, ere the dawn , he bore,
645 Secretly, arms and armour out of store,
Enough for each, and proper to maintain
A battle in the field between the twain.
And in the grove, at time and place they'd set,
Arcita and this Palamon were met.
650 There was no "good-day" given, no saluting,
But without word, rehearsal, or such thing,
Each of them helping, so they armed each other
As dutifully as he were his own brother;
And afterward, with their sharp spears and strong,
655 They thrust each at the other wondrous long.
You might have fancied that this Palamon,

answered thus: "By God that sits above! If you were not sick and mad for love and had a weapon in this place, you'd never move a step out of this grove, but would die by my hand right now. For I renounce the bond and oath which you say that I have made with you. What a fool you are. Love is free to choose and do, and I will have her in spite of all your strength. But in as much as you're a worthy knight and willing to defend your love in armor, hear me now. Tomorrow I will come here armed and outfitted as a knight and will bring arms for you, too, as you will see; and you may choose the better and leave the worse for me. I'll bring enough meat and drink for you this night along with some clothes and bedding. And if it happens that you win my lady and slay me in this forest that I'm now in, then you may have your lady in spite of me."

Palamon replied: "I do agree." And thus they parted until the next morning when each pledged his honor to return. Arcita rode into town later, and before dawn the next morning, he secretly carried all of the weapons and armor that they would need for their battle out of the storehouse. And Arcita and Palamon met in the grove at the time and place according to their agreement. There was no "good-day" given, no saluting, but without a word, rehearsal, or anything, each helped the other to put armor on as dutifully as if each were a brother. And afterward, with their sharp, strong spears, they stabbed at each other for an extraordinarily long time. You might have imagined that Palamon in battle was a furious, mad lion, and that Arcita was quite a tiger. Like wild boars, the two began to fight, like boars that foam at the mouth with anger in the forest. They fought in blood up to their ankles.

In battle, was a furious, mad lion,
And that Arcita was a tiger quite:
Like very boars the two began to smite,
660 Like boars that froth for anger in the wood.
Up to the ankles fought they in their blood.
  Clear was the day, as I have told ere this,
When Theseus, compact of joy and bliss,
With his Hippolyta, the lovely queen,
665 And fair Emilia, clothed all in green,
A-hunting they went riding royally.
And to the grove of trees that grew hard by,
In which there was a hart, as men had told,
Duke Theseus the shortest way did hold.
670 And to the glade he rode on, straight and right,
For there the hart was wont to go in flight,
And over a brook, and so forth on his way.
This duke would have a course at him today,
With such hounds as it pleased him to command.
675 And when this duke was come upon that land,
Under the slanting sun he looked, anon,
And there saw Arcita and Palamon
Who furiously fought, as two boars do;
The bright swords went in circles to and fro
680 So terribly, that even their least stroke
Seemed powerful enough to fell an oak;
But who the two were, nothing did he note.
This duke his courser with the sharp spurs smote
And in one bound he was between the two
685 And lugged his great sword out, and cried out: "Ho!
No more, I say, on pain of losing head!
By mighty Mars, that one shall soon be dead
Who smites another stroke that I may see!
But tell me now what manner of men ye be
690 That are so hardy as to fight out here
Without a judge or other officer,
As if you rode in lists right royally?"
  This Palamon replied, then, hastily,
Saying: "O Sire, what need for more ado?
695 We have deserved our death at hands of you.

The day was clear, as I said before, when Theseus, full of joy and bliss, went hunting with his lovely queen Hippolyta and fair Emily, riding royally dressed all in green. Duke Theseus took the shortest way to a nearby grove of trees in which, as men had told him, there was a deer. And he rode straight on to the glade, for the deer was accustomed to go there fleeing danger, and over a brook, and so forth on his way. The duke would chase at him today with as many hounds as it pleased him to command.

When the Duke rode into the grove, under the sun's rays, he suddenly saw Arcita and Palamon, who fought furiously like two wild boars. The bright swords swung in circles to and fro so terribly that even their least stroke seemed powerful enough to fell an oak tree. But he didn't notice who the two were. This duke struck his horse with his sharp spurs and in one bound he was between the two and lugged his great sword out, and cried: "Stop! No more, I say, or you will loose your heads! By mighty Mars, anyone I see who strikes another blow shall soon be dead. What kind of men are you to be fighting out here with no judges as when you rode in royal tournaments?"

Palamon quickly replied, "Oh Sire, what need for more trouble? We deserve to die at your hands. We are two sorrowful wretches, captives burdened by our own sad lives. Since you are a righteous

117

Two woeful wretches are we, two captives
That are encumbered by our own sad lives;
And as you are a righteous lord and judge
Give us not either mercy or refuge
700   But slay me first, for sacred charity,
But slay my fellow here, as well, with me.
Or slay him first; for though you learn it late,
This is your mortal foe, Arcita—wait!—
That from the land was banished, on his head.
705   And for the which he merits to be dead.
For this is he who came unto your gate,
Calling himself Philostrates—nay, wait!—
Thus has he fooled you well this many a year,
And you have made him your chief squire, I hear:
710   And this is he that loves fair Emily.
For since the day is come when I must die,
I make confession plainly and say on,
That I am that same woeful Palamon
Who has your prison broken, viciously.
715   I am your mortal foe, and it is I
Who love so hotly Emily the bright
That I'll die gladly here within her sight.
      This worthy duke presently spoke again,
Saying: "This judgment needs but a short session:
720   Your own mouth, aye, and by your own confession,
Has doomed and damned you, as I shall record.
There is no need for torture, on my word.
But you shall die, by mighty Mars the red!"
But then the queen, whose heart for pity bled,
725   Began to weep, and so did Emily
And all the ladies in the company.
Great pity must it be, so thought they all,
That ever such misfortune should befall:
For these were gentlemen, of great estate,
730   And for no thing, save love, was their debate.
And all cried out—greater and less, they cried
"Have mercy, lord, upon us women all!"
And down upon their bare knees did they fall,
and would have kissed his feet there where he stood,

lord and judge, do not give us mercy or shelter, but kill me first for holy charity, and also kill my companion here with me. Or kill him first; for though you learn it late, this is your mortal enemy Arcita that was banished from the land on penalty of his head, and for which he deserves to be dead. For this is he who came to your gate calling himself Philostrates. He has fooled you well like this for many years, and I hear you have made him your chief squire. And he loves fair Emily. Since the day has come when I must die, I clearly confess and say that I am that same sorrowful Palamon who has recently escaped from your prison. I am your mortal foe, and it is I who love Emily the bright so dearly that I'll gladly die here in her sight."

The worthy duke spoke again at once, saying: "This is not a difficult decision; for from your own mouth came the confession that doomed you. There is no need for torture, on my word. But by oath to mighty Mars the red, you shall die!" But then the queen, whose heart bled with pity, began to weep, and so did Emily and all the ladies in the company. They all thought that it was a great pity that such a misfortune should occur, for these were gentlemen of noble birth, and their only conflict was over love. And all cried out, "Have mercy, lord, upon all us women." And down upon their bare knees they fell and would have kissed his feet there where he stood until his anger was calmed; for pity soon flows through a gentle heart.

735 Till at the last assuaged was his high mood;
For soon will pity flow through gentle heart.
And though he first for ire did shake and start,
He soon considered, to state the case in brief,
What cause they had for fighting, what for grief;
740 And though his anger still their guilt accused,
Yet in his reason he held them both excused;
In such wise: he thought well that every man
Will help himself in love, if he but can,
And will himself deliver from prison;
745 And, too, at heart he had compassion on
Those women, for they cried and wept as one;
And in his gentle heart he thought anon,
And softly to himself he said then: "Fie
Upon a lord that will have no mercy,
750 But acts the lion, both in word and deed,
To those repentant and in fear and need,
As well as to the proud and pitiless man
That still would do the thing he began!
That lord must surely in discretion lack
755 Who, in such case, can no distinction make,
But weighs both proud and humble in one scale."
    And shortly, when his ire was thus grown pale,
He looked up to the sky, with eyes alight,
And spoke these words, as he would promise plight:
760 "The god of love, ah *benedicite*!
How mighty and how great a lord is he!
Against his might may stand no obstacles,
A true god is he by his miracles;
For he can manage, in his own sweet wise,
765 The heart of anyone as he devise.
Lo, here, Arcita and this Palamon,
That were delivered out of my prison,
And might have lived in Thebes right royally,
Knowing me for their mortal enemy,
770 And also that their lives lay in my hand;
And yet their love has wiled them to this land,
Against all sense, and brought them here to die!
Look you now, is not that a folly high?

And though at first in anger he did rant and rave, he soon considered the reason they had for fighting and for grief. And though
in his anger, he still found them guilty, in his mind, he excused them
both. In reasoning, he understood that every man, if he can, will
help himself in love or to escape from prison. And, too, at heart, he
had compassion on those women, for they cried and wept as one.
And in his gentle heart he thought at once and softly to himself, he
said then, "Shame on a lord that will have no mercy, but acts like the
lion in both word and deed to those who are repentant and in fear
and need and acts as well to the proud and pitiless man that would
do the thing he began! That lord must surely lack good judgment
who, in such case, can make no distinction but instead weighs both
proud and humble on one scale."

And later when his anger had lessened, he looked up to the sky
with shining eyes and spoke these words, as if he made a pledge:
"May the god of love bless us. How mighty and great a lord he is!
By his miracles he is a true god; no obstacle may stand against
his might. He can manage, by his own sweet manner, the heart of
anyone as he wishes. Here are Arcita and this Palamon, who were
delivered from my prison and might have lived royally in Thebes
knowing that I was their mortal enemy and also knowing that their
lives lay in my hand; and yet their love has compelled them to come
to this land against all sense and brought them here to die! Look
now, isn't that a great foolishness? Who can be called a fool, except
he who loves? A man must play the fool, when young or old; I know
it myself from years gone by, for I have been numbered one of love's
servants. Therefore, since I well know all love's pain and how sorely
it can compel man, as one who has been taken in the net, I will forgive and forget your trespass at the plea of my sweet queen, kneeling
here, and of Emily, my dear sister. But you must agree to swear that

Who can be called a fool, except he love?
775 A man must play the fool, when young or old;
I know it of myself from years long gone:
For of love's servants I've been numbered one.
And therefore, since I know well all love's pain,
And know how sorely it can man constrain,
780 As one that has been taken in the net,
I will forgive your trespass, and forget,
At instance of my sweet queen, kneeling here,
Aye, and of Emily, my sister dear.
And you shall presently consent to swear
785 That nevermore will you my power dare,
Nor wage war on me, either night or day,
But will be friends to me in all you may;
I do forgive this trespass, full and fair."
    And then they swore what he demanded there,
790 And, of his might, they of his mercy prayed,
And he extended grace, and thus he said:
"To speak for royalty's inheritress,
Although she be a queen or a princess,
Each of you both is worthy, I confess,
795 When comes the time to wed: but nonetheless
I speak now of my sister Emily,
The cause of all this strife and jealousy—
You know yourselves she may not marry two
At once, although you fight or what you do:
800 One of you, then, and be he loath or lief,
Must pipe his sorrows in an ivy leaf.
That is to say, she cannot have you both,
However jealous one may be, or wroth.
Therefore I put you both in this decree,
805 That each of you shall learn his destiny
As it is cast, and hear, now, in what wise
The word of fate shall speak through my device."
    "My will is this, to draw conclusion flat,
Without reply, or plea, or caveat
810 (In any case, accept it for the best),
That each of you shall follow his own quest,
Free of all ransom or of fear from me;

nevermore will you oppose my power, nor wage war on me, either night or day, but will in all ways be a friend to me. I do forgive this trespass completely."

And they swore to what he demanded and praised his strength and mercy, and he extended favor and thus he said: "To speak for royalty's heiress, although she might be a queen or a princess, each of you is worthy, I confess, when comes the time to wed: but, nonetheless, I speak now for my sister Emily, the cause of all this strife and jealousy—you know yourselves she may not marry two of you at once, despite your fight or what you do. One of you, then, whether he is hated or beloved, must arrange his sorrows in an ivy leaf. That is to say, she cannot have you both, however jealous or angry one may be of the other. Therefore, I put to both of you this decree, so that each of you shall learn his destiny as it is cast; hear, now, in whatever way the word of fate shall speak through my plan.

"To bring about an absolute decision, my command is this, and I do not wish to hear any replies, pleas or threats to it, (in any case, accept it for the best). Each of you shall live his own life free of all ransom and of fear from me; and fifty weeks from now both shall be here once again, each with a hundred knights armed for battle,

And this day, fifty weeks hence, both shall be
Here once again, each with a hundred knights,
815 Armed for the lists, who stoutly for your rights
Will ready be to battle, to maintain
Your claim to love. I promise you, again,
Upon my word, and as l am a knight,
That whichsoever of you wins the fight,
820 That is to say, whichever of you two
May with his hundred, whom I spoke of, do
His foe to death, or out of boundary drive,
Then he shall have Emilia to wive
To whom Fortuna gives so fair a grace."
825   I think that men would deem it negligence
If I forgot to tell of the expense
Of Theseus, who went so busily
To work upon the lists, right royally;
For such an amphitheatre he made,
830 Its equal never yet on earth was laid.
        The day of their return is forthcoming,
When each of them a hundred knights must bring
The combat to support, as I have told;
And into Athens, covenant to uphold,
835 Has each one ridden with his hundred knights,
Well armed for war, at all points, in their mights.
And certainly, 'twas thought by many a man
That never, since the day this world began,
Speaking of good knights hardy of their hands,
840 Wherever God created seas and lands,
Was, of so few, so noble company.
For every man that loved all chivalry,
And eager was to win surpassing fame,
Had prayed to play a part in that great game;
845 And all was well with him who chosen was.
        That Sunday night, ere day began to spring,
When Palamon the earliest lark heard sing,
Although it lacked two hours of being day
Yet the lark sang, and Palamon sang a lay.
850 With pious heart and with a high courage
He rose, to go upon a pilgrimage

to bravely defend your claim to love. I promise you again, upon my word, and as I am a knight, that whichsoever of you wins the fight, that is to say, whichever of you two with his hundred men kills his foe or drives him from the tournament field, then he shall have Emily as his wife, she who Fortune gives so fair a beauty."

I think that men would believe it negligence if I forgot to tell you of the expense Theseus incurred in setting up this tournament. Never on earth was there an amphitheater equal to the one he had built.

So when the day of their return came, both knights rode into Athens to uphold the agreement, each with one hundred knights well-armed for war. And certainly many men thought that never since the day this world began had so noble a company of good knights come from wherever God created seas and lands. For every man that loved chivalry and was eager to gain great fame had prayed to play a part in that great tournament; and all was well with him who was chosen.

It was that Sunday night, before day began to break, when Palamon heard the earliest lark sing two hours before dawn. The lark sang, and Palamon sang a song. With a pious heart and high courage, he rose to go to pay homage to the blessed Cytherea's shrine (I mean the goddess of love, Venus, worthy and kind). At her hour he walked swiftly out to the tournament field where her temple

Unto the blessed Cytherea's shrine
(I mean Queen Venus, worthy and benign).
And at her hour he then walked forth apace
855   Out to the lists wherein her temple was,
And down he knelt in manner to revere,
And from a full heart spoke as you shall hear.
    "Fairest of fair, O lady mine, Venus,
If thou wilt help, thus do I make my vow,
860   To boast of knightly skill I care not now,
Nor do I ask tomorrow's victory,
Nor any such renown, nor vain glory
Of prize of arms, blown before lord and churl,
But I would have possession of one girl,
865   Of Emily, and die in thy service;
Find thou the manner how, and in what wise.
For I care not, unless it better be,
Whether I vanquish them or they do me,
So I may have my lady in my arms.
870   For though Mars is the god of war's alarms,
Thy power is so great in Heaven above,
That, if it be thy will, I'll have my love.
In thy fane will I worship always, so
That on thine altar, where'er I ride or go,
875   I will lay sacrifice and thy fires feed.
And if thou wilt not so, O lady, cede,
I pray thee, that tomorrow, with a spear,
Arcita bear me through the heart, just here.
For I'll care naught, when I have lost my life,
880   That Arcita may win her for his wife.
This the effect and end of all my prayer,
Give me my love, thou blissful lady fair."
    Now when he'd finished all the orison,
His sacrifice he made, this Palamon,
885   Right piously, with all the circumstance,
Albeit I tell not now his observance.
But at the last the form of Venus shook
And gave a sign, and thereupon he took
This as acceptance of his prayer that day.
890   For though the augury showed some delay

was; and he knelt down in a reverent manner, and with a full heart, spoke as you shall hear.

"Fairest of fair, O lady mine, Venus, if you will help me, I make this vow. I have no interest now in boasting of knightly skill, nor do I ask for victory tomorrow, nor for fame or glory; but I would ask for one girl, Emily, as my wife, and die serving you; you decide how and in what way. For I don't care if I defeat them or they defeat me as long as I may have my lady in my arms. For though Mars is the god of war's call to arms, your power is so great in Heaven above that, if it is your will, I'll win my love. I will always worship in your temple, so wherever I ride or go I shall sacrifice and keep the fires burning on your altar. And if you will not, O Venus, grant me my wish, I pray thee that tomorrow Arcita runs me through the heart with a spear. For I will not care, when I've lost my life, that Arcita wins Emily for his wife. This is the end of all my prayer. Give me my love, thou fair blissful lady."

When Palamon had finished his prayer, he made his sacrifices quite devoutly with great detail, although I'll not tell about his ceremony now. But at the end, the statue of Venus shook and gave a sign, and he took this as acceptance of his prayer that day. For though the omen showed some delay, he was still certain his request was granted; so with a glad heart he soon made his way home.

Yet he knew well that granted was his boon;
And with glad heart he got him home right soon.
Three hours unequal after Palamon
To Venus' temple at the lists had gone,
895   Up rose the sun and up rose Emily
And to Diana's temple did she hie.
Her maidens led she thither, and with them
They carefully took fire and each emblem,
And incense, robes, and the remainder all
900   Of things for sacrifice ceremonial.
Her bright hair was unbound, but combed withal;
She wore of green oak leaves a coronal
Upon her lovely head. Then she began
Two fires upon the altar stone to fan.
905   When kindled was the fire, with sober face
Unto Diana spoke she in that place.
      "Chaste goddess, well indeed thou knowest that I
Desire to be a virgin all my life,
Nor ever wish to be man's love or wife.
910   I am, thou know'st, yet of thy company,
A maid, who loves the hunt and venery,
And to go rambling in the greenwood wild,
And not to be a wife and be with child.
I do not crave the company of man.
915   Now help me, lady, since thou may'st and can,
By the three beings who are one in thee.
For Palamon, who bears such love to me,
And for Arcita, loving me so sore,
This grace I pray thee, without one thing more,
920   To send down love and peace between those two,
And turn their hearts away from me: so do
That all their furious love and their desire,
And all their ceaseless torment and their fire
Be quenched or turned into another place;
925   And if it be thou wilt not show this grace,
Or if my destiny be moulded so
That I must needs have one of these same two,
Then send me him that most desires me."

Three hours after Palamon had gone to visit the temple of Venus at the tournament field, the sun rose and Emily got up and hurried to Diana's temple. She led her maidens there and with them they carefully took fire, emblems, incense, robes, and all they needed to conduct a ceremonial sacrifice. Her bright hair was unbound, but combed; she wore a crown of green oak leaves upon her lovely head. Then she began to fan two fires upon the altar. When the fire was lit, Emily spoke with a solemn face to Diana.

"Chaste goddess, you well know that I desire to be a virgin all my life and never wish to be a man's love or wife. As you know, I am, like you, a maid who loves the hunt and the chase, and to go rambling wild in the forest, and not to be a wife and mother. I don't crave the company of man. Help me, lady, since you may and can, by the three beings who are one in thee. For Palamon and Arcita, both who love me greatly, this favor I beg you without one thing more: send down love and peace between the two and turn their hearts away from me, so that their great passion and desire and all their endless torment be extinguished or turned elsewhere. But if you will not show this favor, or if it is my destiny that I must have one of the two, then send me the one who desires me most."

The fires blazed high upon the altar there,
930 While Emily was saying thus her prayer,
But suddenly she saw a sight most quaint,
For there, before her eyes, one fire went faint,
Then blazed again; and after that, anon,
The other fire was quenched, and so was gone.
935 And as it died it made a whistling sound,
As do wet branches burning on the ground,
And from the brands' ends there ran out, anon,
What looked like drops of blood, and many a one;
At which so much aghast was Emily
940 That she was near dazed, and began to cry,
For she knew naught of what it signified;
But only out of terror thus she cried
And wept, till it was pitiful to hear.
But thereupon Diana did appear,
945 With bow in hand, like any right huntress,
And said "My daughter, leave this heaviness.
Among the high gods it has been affirmed,
And by eternal written word confirmed,
That you shall be the wife of one of those
950 Who bear for you so many cares and woes;
But unto which of them I may not tell.
I can no longer tarry, so farewell."
And forth she went in mystic vanishing;
At which this Emily astonished was,
955 And said she then: "Ah, what means this, alas!
I put myself in thy protection here,
Diana, and at thy disposal dear."
And home she wended, then, the nearest way.
This is the purport; there's no more to say.
960   At the next hour of Mars, and following this,
Arcita to the temple walked, that is
Devoted to fierce Mars, to sacrifice
With all the ceremonies, pagan-wise.
With sobered heart and high devotion, on
965 This wise, right thus he said his orison.
"O mighty god that in the regions hold
In every realm and every land

The fires blazed high upon the altar while Emily was saying her prayer, but suddenly she saw a strange sight, for there before her eyes one fire went faint, then blazed again; and after that, instantly, the other fire went out and was gone. And as it died it made a whistling sound as wet branches do when they burn on the ground, and from the ends of the branches there suddenly ran out what looked like many drops of blood. At this sight, Emily was so terrified that she was dazed and began to cry, for she did not know what it all meant. Only out of terror she cried and wept until it was pitiful to hear. But then Diana appeared with a bow in her hand like any real huntress and said: "My daughter, leave this heaviness. Among the gods it has been decreed, and by eternal written word confirmed, that you shall be the wife of one of those who bear for you so many cares and sorrows. But to which of them you will be wed I may not tell. I can no longer stay, so farewell." And forth she went in mystic vanishing; at which Emily was astonished, and then she said, "Ah, what does all this mean, alas! Nevertheless, I put myself in your protection here, Diana, and I am at your disposal." Then home she went, the nearest way. This is the meaning; there's no more to say.

One hour after this, Arcita walked to the temple devoted to fierce Mars, to sacrifice with all the pagan ceremonies. In this manner with sobered heart and high devotion, he said his prayer.

"Oh mighty god who presides over battles, accept from me my pious sacrifice. If my youth may deserve it, and my strength serve

The reins of battle in thy guiding hand,
And givest fortune as thou dost devise,

970   Accept of me my pious sacrifice.
If so it be that my youth may deserve,
And that my strength be worthy found to serve
Have pity, now, upon my pains that smart.
I'm young, and little skilled, as knowest thou,

975   With love more hurt and much more broken now
Than ever living creature was, I'm sure;
For she who makes me all this woe endure,
Whether I float or sink cares not at all,
Now, lord, have pity on my sorrows sore;

980   Give me the victory. I ask no more."
With ended prayer of Arcita the young,
The rings that on the temple door were hung,
And even the doors themselves, rattled so fast
That this Arcita found himself aghast.

985   The fires blazed high upon the altar bright,
Until the entire temple shone with light;
And a sweet odour rose up from the ground;
And Arcita whirled then his arm around,
And yet more incense on the fire he cast,

990   And did still further rites; and at the last
The armour of God Mars began to ring,
And with that sound there came a murmuring,
Low and uncertain, saying: "Victory!"
For which he gave Mars honour and glory.

995   And thus in joy and hope, which all might dare,
Arcita to his lodging then did fare,
Fain of the fight as fowl is of the sun.
But thereupon such quarrelling was begun,
From this same granting, in the heaven above,

1000   Twixt lovely Venus, goddess of all love,
And Mars, the iron god armipotent,
That Jove toiled hard to make a settlement;
Until the sallow Saturn, calm and cold,
Who had so many happenings known of old,

1005   Found from his full experience the art
To satisfy each party and each part.

you, have pity now, upon my pains. I'm young, and little skilled, as you know, and more hurt and more broken than any living creature from love. She for whom I suffer all this pain doesn't care whether I float or sink. Now, lord, have pity on my painful sorrows; give me the victory, I ask no more."

With the prayer of Arcita ended, the rings on the temple door, and even the doors themselves, rattled so fast that Arcita was amazed. The fires blazed high upon the altar, until the entire temple shone with light and a sweet odor rose up from the ground. Arcita whirled his arm around and threw more incense on the fire and did still further rites; with this, the armor of God Mars began to ring, and with the sound came a murmuring, low and uncertain, saying: "Victory!" for which Arcita did thank Mars, and, in joy and hope, Arcita to his lodging then did go, as eager for the fight as the cock is for the sun. But in the heaven above, such quarreling had begun between lovely Venus, goddess of all love, and Mars, the iron god war, that Jove worked hard to reach a settlement. Zeus was not successful until Saturn found, from his experience, the art to satisfy each party. For it is true that age has an advantage; experience and wisdom come with age. Thus Saturn, though not in his nature so to do, devised a plan to quiet all the strife.

For true it is, age has great advantage;
Experience and wisdom come with age;
Thus Saturn, though it scarcely did befit
1010 His nature so to do, devised a plan
To quiet all the strife.
Now will I cease to speak of gods above,
Of Mars and Venus, goddess of all love,
And tell you now, as plainly as I can,
1015 The great result, for which I first began.
A herald on a scaffold cried out "Ho!"
Till all the people's noise was stilled; and so
When he observed that all were fallen still,
He then proclaimed the mighty ruler's will.
1020 "The duke our lord, full wise and full discreet,
Holds that it were but wanton waste to meet
And fight, these gentle folk, all in the guise
Of mortal battle in this enterprise.
Wherefore, in order that no man may die,
1025 He does his earlier purpose modify.
No man, therefore, on pain of loss of life,
Shall any arrow, pole-axe, or short knife
Send into lists in any wise, or bring;
Nor any shortened sword, for point-thrusting,
1030 Shall a man draw, or bear it by his side.
Nor shall a knight against opponent ride,
Save one full course, with any sharp-ground spear;
Unhorsed, a man may thrust with any gear.
And he that's overcome, should this occur,
1035 Shall not be slain, but brought to barrier,
Whereof there shall be one on either side;
Let him be forced to go there and abide.
And if by chance the leader there must go,
Of either side, or slay his equal foe,
1040 No longer, then, shall tourneying endure.
God speed you; go forth now, and lay on sure.
With long sword and with maces fight your fill.
Go now your ways; this is the lord duke's will."
The voices of the people rent the skies,
1045 Such was the uproar of their merry cries:

Now I will tell you no more of the gods above, and instead I'll tell you of the results of which I had begun speaking.

A herald on a scaffold cried out, "Ho!" to quiet all the people's noise; and when he observed that all were fallen still, he proclaimed the mighty Theseus' will. "The duke our lord, both wise and prudent, holds that it would be a foolish waste to have all these gentlemen to meet and to fight a mortal battle in this enterprise. Therefore, in order that no man may die, Theseus does modify his earlier purpose. No man, therefore, on pain of loss of life, shall carry any arrow, pole-axe, or short knife into this tournament. Nor shall he use the point of a shortened sword for point-thrusting, nor shall he draw or bear it by his side. Nor shall a knight ride against an opponent, except for one full course, with any sharp spear; a man knocked from his horse may thrust with any gear, but he that's overcome, should this occur, shall not be slain, but brought to the barriers, of which there is one on either side of the field, and there he shall remain until the battle is over. And if by chance the leader must go there, the tournament shall end. God speed you; go forth now and battle well. With long sword and maces fight your fill. Go now your ways, for this is the lord duke's will."

The voices of the people ripped the skies with an uproar from their merry cries; "Now God save such a lord, who is so good that

"Now God save such a lord, who is so good
He will not have destruction of men's blood!"
Arcita and the hundred of his party
With banner red is entering anon;
1050 And in that self-same moment, Palamon
Is under Venus, eastward in that place,
With banner white, and resolute of face.
In all the world, searching it up and down,
So equal were they all, from heel to crown,
1055 There were no two such bands in any way.
For there was no man wise enough to say
How either had of other advantage
In high repute, or in estate, or age,
So even were they chosen, as I guess.
1060   Then were the gates closed, and the cry rang loud:
"Now do your devoir, all you young knights proud!"
The heralds cease their spurring up and down;
Now ring the trumpets as the charge is blown;
And there's no more to say, for east and west
1065 Two hundred spears are firmly laid in rest;
And the sharp spurs are thrust, now, into side.
Now see men who can joust and who can ride!
Now shivered are the shafts on bucklers thick;
One feels through very breast-bone the spear's prick;
1070 Lances are flung full twenty feet in height;
Out flash the swords like silver burnished bright.
Helmets are hewed, the lacings ripped and shred;
Out bursts the blood, gushing in stern streams red.
With mighty maces bones are crushed in joust.
1075 One through the thickest throng begins to thrust.
There strong steeds stumble now, and down goes all.
One rolls beneath their feet as rolls a ball.
One flails about with club, being overthrown,
Another, on a mailed horse, rides him down.
1080 One through the body's hurt, and haled, for aid,
Spite of his struggles, to the barricade,
As compact was, and there he must abide.
At times Duke Theseus orders them to rest,
To eat a bit and drink what each likes best.

he will not have destruction of men's blood!" With this Arcita and one hundred of his party entered the field with a red banner; and in that same moment, Palamon under Venus's protection entered the field from the East, with a white banner and a firm face. In all the world, searching it up and down, so equal were they that there were no two bands in any other place. There was no man wise enough to say how either had any advantage over the other. In high repute or in estate or age, they were very evenly chosen, as I guess.

After they rode in, the gates were closed and a cry rang out: "Now, you young knights, do your duty and make yourselves proud." With this, the heralds stop their riding up and down and the trumpets blow the signal for the charge. Both East and West, spears are laid in place, the horses are spurred forward, and thus the jousting begins. Shafts are broken on thick shields, and breasts are pricked by spears; lances are flung high in the air and swords flash in the sun. Helmets are cut in shreds as blood gushes out in red streams. In jousts, maces crush the bones. One knight thrusts through the thickest part of the fight.

Horses stumble and some fall down, carrying their riders with them. One fallen rider rolls like a ball beneath the feet of the horses. One fallen rider stands his ground and flails about with his club while a foe on a horse runs into him. One badly injured knight is carried to the barricade, where he has to remain.

At times during the day, Theseus orders the combatants to take a break and get something to eat and drink. And many times that

1085   And many times that day those Thebans two
        Met in the fight and wrought each other woe;
        Unhorsed each has the other on that day.
        No tigress in the vale of Galgophey,
        Whose little whelp is stolen in the light,
1090   Is cruel to the hunter as Arcite
        For jealousy is cruel to Palamon;
        Nor in Belmarie, when the hunt is on
        Is there a lion, wild for want of food,
        That of his prey desires so much the blood
1095   As Palamon the death of Arcite there.
        Their jealous blows fall on their helmets fair;
        Out leaps the blood and makes their two sides red.
            But sometime comes the end of every deed;
        And ere the sun had sunk to rest in gold,
1100   The mighty King Emetreus did hold
        This Palamon, as he fought with Arcita,
        And made his sword deep in the flesh to bite;
        And by the force of twenty men he's made,
        Unyielded, to withdraw to barricade.
1105   And, trying hard to rescue Palamon,
        The mighty King Lycurgus is borne down;
        And King Emetreus, for all his strength,
        Is hurled out of the saddle a sword's length,
        So hits out Palamon once more, or ere
1110   (But all for naught) he's brought to barrier.
        His hardy heart may now avail him naught;
        He must abide there now, being fairly caught
        By force of arms, as by provision known.
            Who sorrows now but woeful Palamon,
1115   Who may no more advance into the fight?
        And when Duke Theseus had seen this sight,
        Unto the warriors fighting, every one,
        He cried out: "Hold! No more! For it is done!
        Now will I prove true judge, of no party.
1120   Theban Arcita shall have Emily,
        Who, by his fortune, has her fairly won."
            But now, what can fair Venus do above?
        What says she now? What does this queen of love

day, Arcita and Palamon fought and knocked each other from their horses. There is no tigress in all of Galgophey, whose cub has been stolen, who is crueler to the hunter than is Arcita to Palamon. Nor in all of Belmarie is there a starved, crazed lion more desirous of blood than Palamon does desire the death of Arcita. The jealous blows of these two fall on each other's helmet causing blood to flow on both sides.

But, in time, comes the end of every action and before the sun sank that night, King Emetreus attacked Palamon as he fought with Arcita. After wounding Palamon, Emetreus and twenty others forced the struggling Palamon toward the barricade. As they did so, King Lycurgus tried to come to Palamon's aid, but it's all for naught, for Lycurgus is knocked down and Palamon is forced to the barricade. When Duke Theseus saw that Palamon had been forced from the battle, he cried out: "Hold! The fight is done. Now I judge that Arcita shall have Emily, whom he has fairly won."

But now, what shall fair Venus far above do? What does she say now? What is this Queen of Love to do—only weep, when her will

But weep so fast, for thwarting of her will,
1125   Her tears upon the lists begin to spill.
She said: "Now am I shamed and over-flung."
But Saturn said: "My daughter, hold your tongue.
Mars has his will, his knight has all his boon,
And, by my head, you shall be eased, and soon."
1130   The hearalds that did loudly yell and cry,
Were at their best for joy of Arcita.
But hear me further while I tell you—ah!—
The miracle that happened there anon.
This fierce Arcita doffs his helmet soon,
1135   And mounted on a horse, to show his face,
He spurs from end to end of that great place,
Looking aloft to gaze on Emily;
And she cast down on him a friendly eye
(For women, generally speaking, go
1140   Wherever Fortune may her favor show);
And she was fair to see, and held his heart.
But from the ground infernal furies start,
From Pluto sent, at instance of Saturn,
Whereat his horse, for fear, began to turn
1145   And leap aside, all suddenly falling there;
And Arcita before he could beware
Was pitched upon the ground, upon his head
And lay there, moving not, as he were dead,
So ran the surging blood into his face.
1150   Anon they carried him from out that place,
With heavy hearts, to Theseus' palace.
There was his harness cut away, each lace,
And swiftly was he laid upon a bed,
For he was yet alive and some words said,
1155   Crying and calling after Emily.
Swells now Arcita's breast until the sore
Increases near his heart yet more and more.
The clotted blood, in spite of all leech-craft,
Rots in his bulk, and there it must be left,
1160   Since no device of skillful blood-letting,
Nor drink of herbs, can help him in this thing.

is so thwarted? She said: "I have been shamed and overruled."

But Saturn said: "My daughter, hold your tongue. Mars has had his way and his knight has won what he desired, but you shall soon have yours."

Then the trumpets blew and the heralds shouted for Arcita's joy. But listen further as I tell—ah— the miracle that happened then. The fierce Arcita removes his helmet, and mounted on his horse he rides about the field looking up to gaze on Emily. And she cast a friendly eye on him. (For women are generally attracted to those whom fortune favors.) And with her beauty, she held Arcita's heart.

But from the ground, Pluto, at Saturn's orders, sends a disturbance which causes Arcita's horse to leap; Arcita, caught unaware, was pitched on the ground where he landed on his head and there he lay not moving, as if dead. With blood from his head running on to his face, they carried Arcita from the field to Theseus' palace. There his armor was cut away, and he was placed upon a bed, for he was still alive and calling out for Emily.

As Arcita lay there, his breast swelled up, and in spite of the leeches that were used, the blood clotted by his heart. Since there are no herbs or other devices to remove the blood, it lay there.

All is so broken in that part of him,
Nature retains no vigour there, nor vim.
The sum of all is, Arcita must die,
1165 And so he sends a word to Emily,
And Palamon, who was his cousin dear;
And then he said to them as you shall hear.
"To you, my lady, whom I love the most;
But I bequeath the service of my ghost
1170 To you above all others, this being sure
Now that my life may here no more endure.
Alas, the woe! Alas, the pain so strong
That I for you have suffered, and so long!
Alas for death! Alas, my Emily!
1175 Alas, the parting of our company!
Alas, my heart's own queen! Alas, my wife!
My soul's dear lady, ender of my life!
Farewell, my sweet foe! O my Emily!
Oh, take me in your gentle arms, I pray,
1180 For love of God, and hear what I will say."
      "I have here, with my cousin Palamon,
Had strife and rancour many a day that's gone,
For love of you and for my jealousy.
May Jove so surely guide my soul for me,
1185 To speak about a lover properly.
In this world, right now, I know of none
So worthy to be loved as Palamon,
Who serves you and will do so all his life.
And if you ever should become a wife,
1190 Forget not Palamon, the noble man."
      And with that word his speech to fail began,
For from his feet up to his breast had come
The cold of death, making his body numb.
And furthermore, from his two arms the strength
1195 Was gone out, now, and he was lost, at length.
Only the intellect, and nothing more,
Which dwelt within his heart so sick and sore,
Began to fail now, when the heart felt death,
And his eyes darkened, and he failed of breath.
1200 But on his lady turned he still his eye,

142

All the natural defenses in that part of him being broken, he loses all his vim and vigor. The sum of it is that Arcita must die, and so he asks both Emily and Palamon to come to him. Then he said as you shall hear: "To you, my lady, whom I love the most, I bequeath the service of my ghost, for it is clear that I shall not live. Alas, the sorrow and pain I have suffered for you. Alas that my death shall now part us. Farewell my sweet foe, my Emily! Take me in your arms and for the love of God, hear what I have to say.

"Between my cousin Palamon and myself there has been much bitterness and jealousy over you. Now may Jove quiet my soul that I may speak about a lover properly. In this world right now I know of no one so worthy to be loved as Palamon. If you ever should become his wife, he will serve you all his life, so when you consider taking a husband, do not forget the noble Palamon."

And with that his speech began to fail for death crept up his body, leaving it numb and cold. And, furthermore, his arms fell limp as he lost his strength. Now the spirit which lived within him began to fail and his eyes darkened and his breathing faltered, but on his lady he turned his eye, and his last word was "Mercy, Emily!" With this, his soul departed his body, to go where I cannot say. Now will I speak of Emily.

And his last word was, "Mercy, Emily!"
His spirit changed its house and went from here.
As I was never there, I cannot say where.
Now will I speak forthwith of Emily.

1205   Shrieked Emily and howled now Palamon,
Till Theseus his sister took, anon,
And bore her, swooning, for the corpse away.
How shall it help, to dwell the livelong day
In telling how she wept both night and morrow?

1210 For in like cases women have such sorrow,
When their good husband from their side must go,
And, for the greater part, they take on so,
Or else they fall into such malady
That, at the last, and certainly, they die.

1215   Infinite were the sorrows and the tears
Of all old folk and folk of tender years
Throughout the town, at death of this Theban;
For him there wept the child and wept the man;
So great a weeping was not, 'tis certain,

1220 When Hector was brought back, but newly slain,
To Troy. Alas, the sorrow that was there!
Tearing of cheeks and rending out of hair.
"Oh why will you be dead," these women cry,
"Who had of gold enough, and Emily?"

1225 No man might comfort then Duke Theseus,
Excepting his old father, Aegeus,
Who knew this world's mutations, and men's own,
Since he had seen them changing up and down,
Joy after woe, and woe from happiness:

1230 He showed them, by example, the process.
     "Just as there never died a man," quoth he,
"But he had lived on earth in some degree,
Just so there never lived a man," he said,
"In all this world, but must be sometime dead.

1235 This world is but a thoroughfare of woe,
And we are pilgrims passing to and fro;
Death is the end of every worldly sore."
And after this, he told them yet much more
To that effect, all wisely to exhort

Palamon howled and Emily shrieked until Theseus took her in his arms and led her away. How will it help if I now tell you how she wept continually night and day? For in such cases, women have great sorrow when their husbands die, and most of the time they carry on so or else fall gravely ill and, at last, die.

Great were the sorrows and the tears of both the young and old people throughout the town at the death of Arcita. Every man, woman and child wept for him. When Hector was slain and his body brought back to Troy, it is certain there was no greater weeping. So great was this sorrow! Many tears flowed and women, in their grief, pulled at their hair. These women cry, "Oh why are you dead Arcita; you who had gold enough and Emily's heart?"

Duke Theseus could not be comforted by anyone except his father, Aegeus, who knew how the things of this world change. Aegeus had seen life change; he had seen fortune go up and down. He had seen joy follow sorrow, and sorrow follow happiness. He showed them all of this, by this example.

"Just as there never died a man," said he, "who had not first lived in some degree, there never lived a man, who must not at some time die. This world is but a highway of sorrow, and we are pilgrims traveling back and forth with death at the end of our worldly pain." And then Aegeus said much more to this effect, and in this way, he urged the people to find some comfort from their grief.

145

1240 The people that they should find some comfort.
Duke Theseus now considered and with care
What place of burial he should prepare
For good Arcita, as it best might be,
And one most worthy of his high degree.
1245 And at the last concluded, hereupon,
That where at first Arcita and Palamon
Had fought for love, with no man else between,
There in that very grove, so sweet and green,
Where he mused on his amorous desires
1250 Complaining of love's hot and flaming fires,
He'd make a pyre and have the funeral.
Accomplished there, and worthily in all.
And so he gave command to hack and hew
The ancient oaks, and lay them straight and true
1255 In split lengths that would kindle well and burn.
His officers, with sure swift feet, they turn
And ride away to do his whole intent.
And after this Duke Theseus straightway sent
For a great bier, and had it all o'er-spread
1260 With cloth of gold, the richest that he had.
Arcita clad he, too, in cloth of gold;
White glove were on his hands where they did fold;
Upon his head a crown of laurel green,
And near his hand a sword both bright and keen.
1265 Then, having bared the dead face on the bier,
The duke so wept,'twas pitiful to hear.
And, so that folk might see him, one and all,
When it was day he brought them to the hall
Which echoed of their wailing cries anon.
1270 Then came this woeful Theban, Palamon,
With fluttery beard and matted, ash-strewn hair,
All in black clothes wet with his tears; and there,
Surpassing all in weeping, Emily,
The most affected of the company.
1275 The noblest Greeks did gladly volunteer
To bear upon their shoulders that great bier,
With measured pace and eyes gone red and wet,
Through all the city, by the wide main street,

Duke Theseus now carefully considered what place of burial he should prepare for Arcita. And at last he concluded, that where Arcita and Palamon first had fought for love, Arcita should be buried; there, in that sweet and green grove, where he mused on his amorous desires and complained of love's hot and flaming fires. In that spot, he would make a pyre to have the funeral; and so he gave the command to cut down the ancient oaks, and lay them straight and true in split lengths so they would burn easily. His officers swiftly rode off to do his bidding. And after this Duke Theseus sent for a great casket, and had it covered with cloth of gold, the richest that he had. Arcita, also, he dressed in a cloth of gold and upon his head he placed a crown of green, and near his hand a sharp sword. Then, in looking at Arcita's face, the duke wept so, it was pitiful to hear. And, so that all folks might see Arcita when it was day, he brought them to the hall, which echoed from their cries. Then came the woeful Palamon, with fluttery beard and matted hair. He was dressed all in black clothes that were wet with his tears; but surpassing all in weeping was Emily, the most affected of all those present.

The noblest Greeks gladly volunteered to carry Arcita's casket, with measured pace and eyes gone red and wet, through all the city, by the wide main street, which was all spread with black, and covered with this same cloth were all the houses. Upon the right,

Which was all spread with black, and, wondrous high,
1280 Covered with this same cloth were houses nigh.
Upon the right hand went old Aegeus,
And on the other side Duke Theseus,
With vessels in their hands, of gold right fine,
All filled with honey, milk, and blood, and wine;
1285 And Palamon with a great company;
And after that came woeful Emily,
With fire in hands, as use was, to ignite
The sacrifice and set the pyre alight.
    Great labour and full great apparelling
1290 Went to the service and the fire-making.
That is to say, the branches went so wide.
Full many a load of straw they did provide.
But how the fire was made to climb so high;
Or what names all the different trees went by,
1295 Or how they were felled, shan't be told by me.
Nor how aghast the ground was in the light,
Not being used to seeing the sun so bright;
Nor how the fire was started first with straw,
And then with dry wood, riven thrice by saw,
1300 And then with green wood and with spicery,
And then with cloth of gold and jewelery
And garlands hanging with full many a flower,
And myrrh, and incense, sweet as rose in bower;
Nor how Arcita lies among all this,
1305 Nor what vast wealth about his body is;
Nor how this Emily, as was their way,
Lighted the sacred funeral fire, that day,
Nor how she swooned when men built up the fire,
Nor what she said, nor what was her desire;
1310 No, nor what gems men on the fire then cast,
When the white flame went high and burned so fast;
Nor how one cast his shield, and one his spear,
And some their vestments, on that burning bier,
With cups of wine, and cups of milk, and blood,
1315 Into that flame, which burned as wild-fire would;
Nor how the Greeks, in one huge wailing rout,
Rode slowly three times all the fire about,

Old Aegeus walked and on the other side Duke Theseus, with gold vessels in their hands, all filled with honey, milk, and blood, and wine; then came Palamon with a great company; and after that came woeful Emily carrying a fire in hands, which was to be used to ignite the sacrifice and set the pyre alight.

A great labor went into the preparation of the fire-making, that is to say, many branches and many a full load of straw they did provide. But how the fire was made to climb so high; or what names all the different trees went by, or how they were felled, shan't be told by me. Nor how surprised the ground was in the light, not being used to seeing the sun so bright; nor how the fire was started first with straw and then with dry wood and then with green wood and with spices, and then with cloth of gold and jewelry and garlands hanging with many flowers and myrrh and incense, sweet as a rose in a bower; nor how Arcita lies among all this, nor what vast wealth lies about his body; nor how this Emily, as was their way, lighted the sacred funeral fire that day, nor how she swooned when men built up the fire, nor what she said, nor what was her desire; no, nor what gems men threw on the fire then. Nor how one threw on his shield, and one his spear, and some threw their garments, onto that burning casket, with cups of wine, and cups of milk and blood into that flame, which burned as wild-fire would; nor how the Greeks in one huge wailing cry rode slowly three times around the fire, upon the left hand, with a loud shouting, and three times more, with weapons clattering, while the women present raised up a great cry; nor shall I tell how homeward sad Emily was led; nor how Arcita burned until he was but cold ashes. Nor how the Greeks played all that night, nor who it was that, naked, wrestled best, nor who it was that best bore himself in appointed deeds. I will not even tell how they all went home to Athens, when the play was done; but I will get briefly to the point, now, and make an end of this lengthy tale.

Upon the left hand, with a loud shouting,
And three times more, with weapons clattering,
1320   While thrice the women there raised up a cry;
Nor how was homeward led sad Emily;
Nor how Arcita burned to ashes cold;
All that same night, nor how the Greeks did play
Who, naked, wrestled best, with oil anointed,
1325   Nor who best bore himself in deeds appointed.
I will not even tell how they were gone
Home, into Athens, when the play was done;
But briefly to the point, now, will I wend
And make of this, my lengthy tale, an end.
1330   With passing in their length of certain years,
All put by was the mourning and the tears
Of Greeks, as by one general assent;
And then it seems there was a parliament
At Athens, upon certain points in case;
1335   Among the which points spoken of there was
The ratifying of alliances
That should hold Thebes from all defiances.
Whereat this noble Theseus, anon,
Invited there the gentle Palamon,
1340   Not telling him what was the cause and why;
But in his mourning clothes, and sorrowfully,
He came upon that bidding, so say I.
And then Duke Theseus sent for Emily.
When they were seated and was hushed the place,
1345   And Theseus had mused a little space,
Ere any word came from his full wise breast,
His two eyes fixed on whoso pleased him best,
Then with a sad face sighed he deep and still,
And after that began to speak his will.
1350   "When first God forged the goodly chain of love,
Great the effect, and high was His intent;
Well knew He why, and what thereof He meant;
For with that goodly chain of love He bound
The fire, the air, the water, and dry ground
1355   In certain bounds, the which they might not flee;
That same First Cause and Mover," then quoth he,

When a number of years passed, all the mourning and the tears were stopped. At Athens, there was a meeting of the parliament upon certain points. Among the points they spoke of was the ratifying of alliances that should hold back Thebes from defying Athens. To this meeting, the noble Theseus invited gentle Palamon, not telling him what was the reason for the invitation. Nevertheless Palamon, in his mourning clothes and sorrowful, came as requested. And then Duke Theseus sent for Emily. When all were seated and the place hushed, before he spoke, Theseus stared thoughtfully on those who pleased him best. Then with a sad face he deeply sighed and after that began to speak his will.

"When God first forged the chain of love, the effect was great, and His intent was lofty. He knew well why and what He meant to do; for with that chain of love, He bound the fire, the air, the water, and dry ground in such a way that they might not flee. God, the First Cause and Mover," then said he, "has established a certain length of days that all creatures born in this world may call their own, beyond which, not by one day may they live, though, all may

"Has stablished in this base world, up and down,
A certain length of days to call their own
For all that are engendered in this place,
1360 Beyond the which not one day may they pace,
Though yet all may that certain time abridge;
Authority there needs none, I allege,
For it is well proved by experience.
Well may man know, unless he be a fool
1365 That every part derives but from the whole,
And therefore, of His Wisdom's Providence,
Has He so well established ordinance
That species of all things and all progressions,
If they'd endure, it must be by successions,
1370 Not being themselves eternal, 'tis no lie:
This may you understand and see by eye."

   "Lo now, the oak, that has long nourishing
Even from the time that it begins to spring,
And has so long a life, as we may see,
1375 Yet at the last all wasted is the tree.
"Consider, too, how even the hard stone
Under our feet we tread each day upon
Yet wastes it, as it lies beside the way.
And the broad river will be dry some day.
1380 And great towns wane; we see them vanishing.
Thus may we see the end to everything."

   "Of man and woman just the same is true:
Needs must, in either season of the two,
That is to say, in youth or else in age,
1385 All men perish, the king as well as page;
Some in their bed, and some in the deep sea,
And some in the wide field—as it may be;
There's naught will help; all go the same way. Aye,
Then may I say that everything must die.
1390 Who causes this but Jupiter the King?
He is the Prince and Cause of everything,
Converting all back to that primal well
From which it was derived, 'tis sooth to tell.
And against this, for every thing alive,
1395 Of any state, avails it not to strive.

cut short that time; I need not quote an authority to prove this, for it is well proved by experience. Any man who is not a fool knows that every part derives from the whole, and, therefore, God in his wisdom has established that all species if they'd endure, it must be by succession, not being themselves eternal. This may you understand and see by your own eye.

"Look at the oak that has so long a life, as we may see, yet even this old oak tree must, at the last, also die. Consider, too, how even the hard stone under our feet, which we walk upon each day, eventually crumbles. And the broad river some day will be dry, and even great towns we see vanish. Thus may we see that there is an end to everything.

"Of man and woman just the same is true: either in youth or else in age, all men perish, the king as well as his page; Some die in their bed, and some in the deep sea, and some in the wide field—as it may be; there's nothing that will help, for we all go the same way. Then may I say that everything must die. Who causes this but Jupiter the King? He is the Prince and Cause of everything, who converts all that exists back to that dust from which it had come. For every thing that lives, it is useless to strive against this.

"Then is it wisdom, as it seems to me,
To make a virtue of necessity,
And calmly take what we may not eschew,
And specially that which to all is due.
1400 Whoso would balk at aught, he does folly,
And thus rebels against His potency.
And certainly a man has most honour
In dying in his excellence and flower,
When he is certain of his high good name;
1405 For then he gives to friend, and self, no shame.
And gladder ought a friend be of his death
When, in much honour, he yields up his breath,
Than when his name's grown feeble with old age;
For all forgotten, then, is his courage.
1410 Hence it is best for all of noble name
To die when at the summit of their fame.
The contrary of this is wilfulness.
Why do we grumble? Why have heaviness
That good Arcita, chivalry's fair flower,
1415 Is gone, with honour, in his best-lived hour,
Out of the filthy prison of this life?
Why grumble here his cousin and his wife
About his welfare, who loved them so well?
Can he thank them? Nay, God knows, not! Nor tell
1420 How they his soul and their own selves offend."
    "What may I prove by this long argument
Save that we all turn to merriment,
After our grief, and give Jove thanks for grace.
And so, before we go from out this place,
1425 I counsel that we make, of sorrows two,
One perfect joy, lasting for aye, for you;
And look you now, where most woe is herein,
There will we first amend it and begin.
    "Sister," quoth he, "you have my full consent,
1430 With the advice of this my Parliament,
That gentle Palamon, your own true knight,
Who serves you well with will and heart and might,
And so has ever, since you knew him first—
That you shall, of your grace, allay his thirst

"Then since this is so, it is wisdom, as it seems to me, to make a virtue of necessity and to calmly accept what we may not avoid, especially that which must happen to us all. He who would balk at this is foolish, for in so doing, he thus rebels against God's power. And certainly a man has the most honor when he dies in his prime when he is certain of his high good name and he gives to friend and self no shame. And gladder ought a person be when a young friend dies in his prime, in contrast to when a friend's name is grown feeble with old age, and all have forgotten his courage. Hence, it is best for all of noble name to die when at the height of their fame. To act against this is willfulness. Why do we grumble? Why have sorrow that Arcita, chivalry's fair flower, has gone with honor in his best-lived hour and escaped from the filthy prison of this life? Then why do his cousin and his wife complain about his welfare? Can he thank them? Not a bit! Nor can he tell them how they offend his soul and their own selves.

"What may I prove by this long argument except that after our grief, we all must turn to merriment and give Jove thanks for grace. And so, before we leave this place, I counsel that we make of two sorrows, one perfect joy for both of you; and look you now to the one with greatest sorrow, for there will we first begin to make a change.

"Sister," said he to Emily, "you have my full consent, and the advice of Parliament that gentle Palamon, your own true knight, he who serves you well with will and heart and might, and has so ever since you first knew him—that it is he you shall take for lord and husband. Lend me your hand because this is our agreement, so let your woman's pity make him glad. For he is a king's brother's son,

155

1435   By taking him for husband and for lord:
Lend me your hand, for this is our accord.
Let now your woman's pity make him glad.
For he is a king's brother's son, by gad;
And though he were a poor knight bachelor,
1440   Since he has served you for so many a year,
And borne for you so great adversity,
This ought to weigh with you, it seems to me,
For mercy ought to dominate mere right."
    Then said he thus to Palamon the knight:
1455   "I think there needs but little sermoning
To make you give consent, now, to this thing.
Come near, and take your lady by the hand."
Between them, then, was tied that nuptial band,
Which is called matrimony or marriage,
1450   By all the council and the baronage.
And thus, in all bliss and with melody,
Has Palamon now wedded Emily.
And God, Who all this universe has wrought,
Send him His love, who has it dearly bought.
1455   For now has Palamon, in all things, wealth,
Living in bliss, in riches, and in health;
And Emily loved him so tenderly,
And he served her so well and faithfully,
That never word once marred their happiness,
1460   No jealousy, nor other such distress.
Thus ends now Palamon and Emily;
And may God save all this fair company! Amen.

by heaven; and though he were a poor knight bachelor, since he has served you for so many a year, and has borne for you so great adversity, this ought to weigh with you in his favor, for mercy ought to dominate mere right."

Then he said to Palamon, "I think there needs little to be said in order to get you to give consent to this thing. Come near, and take your lady by the hand."

Between them then was tied that nuptial band, which is called matrimony or marriage, and thus, in all bliss and with melody, has Palamon now married Emily. And may God, the maker of all this universe, send him His love. For now Palamon is wealthy in all things, living in bliss, in riches, and in health; and Emily who loved him so tenderly, he served her well and faithfully. Not one word ever marred their happiness, no jealousy, nor other such distress. Thus ends the tale of Palamon and Emily; and may God save all this fair company! Amen.

Comprehension Check

1. Why is this an appropriate tale for the knight to tell?

2. After they are imprisoned, the two knights see Emily; what happens to the relationship between the cousins as a result of their feelings for Emily?

3. In the scene when Arcita and Palamon first lay eyes on Emily, what aspects of the code of courtly love do we see?

4. How does Arcita come to be released? What are the conditions of Arcita's release?

5. What does Arcita say about the role of fate in the lives of men?

6. Released from prison and now at home, what physical changes take place in Arcita? Why?

7. While some modern readers may find the story of Arcita implausible, why would the pilgrims in Canterbury not find it unusual?

8. What happens to Arcita during the three years after he has the dream about Mercury?

9. Hiding in a grove, Palamon overhears Arcita's lament. Explain his point in the section below:

   Love has his fiery dart so burningly
   Struck through my faithful and care-laden heart,
   My death was patterned ere my swaddling-shirt.
   You slay me with your two eyes, Emily;
   You are the cause for which I now must die.

10. Explain the gist of the following lines:

> Great destiny, minister-general,
> That executes in this world, and for all,
> The needs that God foresaw ere we were born,
> So strong it is that, though the world had sworn
> The contrary of a thing, by yea or nay,
> Yet sometime it shall fall upon a day,
> Though not again within a thousand years.
> For certainly our wishes and our fears,
> Whether of war or peace, or hate or love,
> All, all are ruled by that Foresight above.

11. Palamon prays to Venus, Emily prays to Diana, and Arcita prays to Mars; all of them are praying for contradictory things. What answers do they appear to receive with regard to their prayers?

12. What advice does Aegeus give Theseus?

13. How does the tale end?

Essay Questions

1. After finishing this tale, what would you infer is involved in the code of chivalry?

2. Discuss the theme of friendship in its various forms as it is seen in this tale.

3. Why do you suppose that Chaucer decided to use ancient Greece as the setting for *The Knight's Tale*? Support your generalizations with examples from the text.

4. Explain what the code of courtly love involves and illustrate your explanation with examples from the text.

5. What is Chaucer's view in regard to fate or Divine Providence?

The Pardoner's Tale

IN FLANDERS, ONCE, there was a company
Of young companions given to folly,
Riot and gambling, brothels and taverns;
And, to the music of harps, lutes, gitterns,
5   They danced and played at dice both day and night,
And ate also and drank beyond their might,
Whereby they made the devil's sacrifice
Within that devil's temple, wicked wise,
By superfluity both vile and vain.
10   So damnable their oaths and so profane
That it was terrible to hear them swear;
Our blessed Saviour's Body did they tear;
They thought the Jews had rent Him not enough;
And each of them at others' sins would laugh.
15   Then entered dancing-girls of ill repute,
Graceful and slim, and girls who peddled fruit,
Harpers and bawds and women selling cake,
Who do their office for the Devil's sake,
To kindle and blow the fire of lechery,
20   Which is so closely joined with gluttony;
I call on holy writ, now, to witness
That lust is in all wine and drunkenness.
O gluttony, of you we may complain!
Oh, knew a man how many maladies
25   Follow on excess and on gluttonies,
Surely he would be then more moderate
In diet, and at table more sedate.
Alas! A foul thing is it, by my fay,
To speak this word, and fouler is the deed,
30   When man so guzzles of the white and red
That of his own throat makes he his privy,

The Pardoner's Tale

IN FLANDERS, THERE was once a group of young men who were prone to the foolish conduct of fighting and gambling and going to brothels and taverns. Dancing to the music of harps, lutes, and guitars, they tossed dice day and night and ate and drank beyond their capacity; and in so doing, they made sacrifice to the devil in wicked ways with their evil and worthless overindulgence. Their oaths were so damnable and so full of contempt for sacred things that it was terrible to hear them swear. Our blessed Lord's body they tore apart with their oaths; they thought the Jews had not torn Him enough. They would laugh at each other's sins. Then entered the graceful, slim dancing girls of ill repute, and the girls who peddled fruit, the minstrels and prostitutes, and women selling cake, all who do the Devil's work by kindling and enflaming the sexual desire which is so closely connected with gluttony. I call on the Bible, now, as witness that lust comes from wine and drunkenness.

O gluttony, of you we may well complain! O, if a man knew how many illnesses are caused by overindulgence, and eating and drinking too much, he would have a more moderate diet and be sober at the table. Alas! A foul thing it is, by my faith, to speak this word, gluttony, and fouler is the deed, when a man drinks so much white and red wine that he turns his own throat into a toilet because of this cursed overindulgence. To be honest, a person who gives in to such pleasures is really dead while he is absorbed with this vice. Wine is a lustful thing, and drunkenness is full of conflict and

Because of this cursed superfluity.
But truly, he that such delights entice
Is dead while yet he wallows in this vice.
35 A lecherous thing is wine, and drunkenness
Is full of striving and of wretchedness.
O drunken man, disfigured is your face,
Sour is your breath, foul are you to embrace,
You fall down just as if you were stuck swine;
40 Your tongue is loose, your honest care obscure;
For drunkenness is very sepulture
Of any mind a man may chance to own.
In whom strong drink has domination shown
He can no counsel keep for any dread.
45 Now keep you from the white and from the red.
    And now that I have told of gluttony,
I'll take up gambling, showing you thereby
The curse of chance, and all its evils treat;
From it proceeds false swearing and deceit,
50 Blaspheming, murder, and—what's more—the waste
of time and money; add to which, debased
And shamed and lost to honour quite is he,
Who once a common gambler's known to be.
And ever the higher one is of estate,
55 The more he's held disgraced and desolate.
And if a prince plays similar hazardry
In all his government and policy,
He loses in the estimate of men
His good repute, and finds it not again.
60 Now these three roisterers, whereof I tell,
Long before prime was rung by any bell,
Were sitting in a tavern for to drink;
And as they sat they heard a small bell clink
Before a corpse being carried to his grave;
65 Whereat one of them called unto his knave:
"Go run," said he, "and ask them civilly
What corpse it is that's just now passing by,
And see that you report the man's name well."
    "Sir," said the boy, "it needs not that they tell.
70 I learned it, ere you came here, full two hours;

unhappiness. O drunken man, your face is distorted, your breath is sour, and you are disgusting to embrace. You fall down like a stuck pig, you cannot speak clearly, and your decent appearance is lost. For drunkenness is the very tomb in which any intelligence a man may have is buried. There is no doubt that he who is controlled by drink can keep no secrets. Now stay away from the white and from the red wine.

And now that I have spoken of gluttony, I'll talk about gambling and discuss all its evils; from it comes lying and deceit, swearing against God, murder, and, what's more, the waste of time and money; furthermore, once a man's known to be a common gambler, he is shamed and dishonored. And the higher one's class, the greater he is held in disgrace and ruin. And if a prince gambles in government and policy, he loses his good reputation in the judgment of men, and he will not get it back again.

Long before the bell which rings at nine in the morning was rung, three revelers of whom I speak were sitting in a tavern drinking; and as they sat there, they heard that small processional bell rung which precedes a corpse as it is being carried to his grave. One of the three then called to his serving boy, "Go quickly and ask them politely who that corpse is just now passing by."

"Sir," said the boy, "they do not have to tell me that. I learned that information two hours ago before you came here. He was, by

He was, by gad, an old comrade of yours;
And he was slain, all suddenly, last night,
When drunk, as he sat on his bench upright;
An unseen thief, called Death, came stalking by,
75 Who hereabouts makes all the people die,
And with his spear he clove his heart in two
And went his way and made no more ado.
He's slain a thousand with this pestilence;
And, master, ere you come in his presence,
80 It seems to me to be right necessary
To be forewarned of such an adversary:
Be ready to meet him for evermore.
My mother taught me this, I say no more."
   "By holy Mary," said the innkeeper,
85 "The boy speaks truth, for Death has slain, this year,
A mile or more hence, in a large village,
Both man and woman, child and hind and page.
I think his habitation must be there;
To be advised of him great wisdom 'twere,
90 Before he did a man some dishonour."
   "Yea, by God's arms!" exclaimed this roisterer,
"Is it such peril, then, this Death to meet?
I'll seek him in the road and in the street,
As I now vow to God's own noble bones!
95 Hear, comrades, we're of one mind, as each owns;
Let each of us hold up his hand to other
And each of us become the other's brother,
And we three will go slay this traitor Death;
He shall be slain who's stopped so many a breath,
100 By God's great dignity, ere it be night."
Together did these three their pledges plight
To live and die, each of them for the other,
As if he were his very own blood brother.
And up they started, drunken, in this rage,
105 And forth they went, and towards that village
Whereof the innkeeper had told before.
And so, with many a grisly oath, they swore
And Jesus' blessed body once more rent—
"Death shall be dead if we find where he went."

heaven, an old friend of yours; and he was killed suddenly last night while he was drunk and as he sat upright on his bench. An unseen thief called Death, who makes all the people around here die, came stalking. With his spear he cut his heart in two, and he left without saying anything. He has killed a thousand with this plague; and, master, before you come in Death's presence, I must warn you of such an adversary; be ready to meet him any time. My mother taught me this, I say no more."

"By holy Mary," said the innkeeper, "the boy is telling the truth, for this year Death has slain both man and woman, child and servant and page in a large village a mile or so from here. I think he lives over there. It would be wise to be warned of him before he does a man some harm."

"Ha, by God!" said the merrymaker, "Is it so dangerous, then, to meet Death? I swear to God, I will look for him on the highways and the streets. Listen friends, let the three of us join together, and we will make a pledge to each other that with God's help, before it is night, we will find and kill this traitor Death, who has stopped so many a breath." So together the three pledged to live and die for each other, just as though they were really brothers. And in their drunken madness they jumped up and headed toward the village the innkeeper had told them about.

And so they swore many grisly oaths and tore apart Jesus' blessed body once more: "Death shall be dead if we find where he went." When they had gone about half a mile, just as they were about to go

165

110   When they had gone not fully half a mile,
Just as they would have trodden over a stile,
An old man, and a poor , with them did meet.
This ancient man full meekly them did greet,
And said thus: "Now, lords, God keep you and see!"

115   The one that was most insolent of these three
Replied to him: "What? Churl of evil grace,
Why are you all wrapped up, except your face?
Why do you live so long in so great age?"
      This ancient man looked upon his visage

120   And thus replied: "Because I cannot find
A man, nay, though I walked from here to Ind,
Either in town or country who'll engage
To give his youth in barter for my age;
And therefore must I keep my old age still,

125   As long a time as it shall be God's will.
Not even Death, alas! my life will take;
Thus restless I my wretched way must make
But, sirs, in you it is no courtesy
To speak to an old man despitefully,

130   Unless in word he trespass or in deed.
In holy writ you may, yourselves, well read
'Before an old man, hoar upon the head,
You should arise.' Which I advise you read,
Nor to an old man any injury do

135   More than you would that men should do to you
In age, if you so long time shall abide;
And God be with you, whether you walk or ride.
I must pass on now where I have to go."
      "Nay, ancient churl, by God it sha'n't be so,"

140   Cried out this other hazarder, anon;
"You sha'n't depart so easily, by Saint John!
You spoke just now of that same traitor Death,
Who in this country stops our good friends' breath
Hear my true word, since you are his own spy,

145   Tell where he is or you shall rue it, aye
By God and by the holy Sacrament!
Indeed you must be, with this Death, intent
To slay all us young people, you false thief."

through a gate, they met a poor old man who greeted them humbly and said, "God bless you and protect you!"

The most arrogant of the revelers replied, "What? Peasant, why is all but your face so wrapped up? Why do you live to such a great age?"

This ancient man looked upon the other man's face and replied: "Because, even though I walked from here to India, I cannot find anyone in either town or country who will agree to give his youth in exchange for my old age; therefore I must keep my old age for as long as it shall be God's will. Not even Death, alas, will take my life. So I have to walk around like this all day. But, sirs, it is not courteous to talk to an old man with contempt unless he wrongs you by word or deed. In the Bible you yourselves may read, 'Before an old man with gray hair, you should rise,' which I advise you to read. Nor should you harm an old man, any more than you would have men do so to you when you are old, if you shall live so long. Now, God be with you wherever you walk or ride. I must be on my way to where I have to go."

"Oh no, old man, by God, you shall not go!" said one of the gamblers immediately. "You will not get away so easily, by Saint John! You just spoke of that traitor Death, who is killing our friends in this country. Since you are his spy, you will tell us where he is or, by God and by the holy Sacrament, take my word for it, you will regret it! Indeed, you and Death must be intent on killing all of us young people, you false thief."

"Now, sirs," said he, "if you're so keen, in brief,
150 to find out Death, turn up this crooked way,
For in that grove I left him, by my fay,
Under a tree, and there he will abide;
Nor for your boasts will he a moment hide.
See you that oak? Right there you shall him find.
155 God save you, Who redeemed all humankind,
And mend your ways!"—thus said this ancient man.
And every one of these three roisterers ran
Till he came to that tree; and there they found,
Of florins of fine gold, new-minted, round,
160 Well-nigh eight bushels full, or so they thought.
No longer, then, after this Death they sought,
But each of them so glad was of that sight,
Because the florins were so fair and bright,
That down they all sat by this precious hoard.
165 The worst of them was first to speak a word.
"Brothers," said he, "take heed to what I say;
My wits are keen, although I mock and play.
This treasure here Fortune to us has given
That mirth and jollity our lives may liven,
170 And easily as it's come, so will we spend.
But might this gold be carried from this place
Home to my house, or if you will, to yours—
For well we know that all this gold is ours—
Then were we all in high felicity.
175 But certainly by day this may not be;
For men would say that we were robbers strong,
And we'd, for our own treasure, hang ere long.
This treasure must be carried home by night
All prudently and slyly, out of sight.
180 So I propose that cuts among us all
Be drawn, and let's see where the cut will fall;
And he that gets the short cut, blithe of heart
Shall run to town at once, and to the mart,
And fetch us bread and wine here, privately.
185 And two of us shall guard, right cunningly,
This treasure well; and if he does not tarry,
When it is night we'll all the treasure carry

"Now sirs," said he, "if you are so eager to meet Death, turn up this crooked path, for I left him, by my faith, in that grove under a tree, and there he will remain. He will not hide for a moment because of your boasts. Do you see that oak? He will be there. May God, who redeemed all humankind, save you and mend your ways!"—thus said this ancient man.

So each of the scoundrels ran until he came to that tree, and there they found about eight bushels full of fine, newly-minted gold coins. Then they no longer searched for Death. Each of them was so happy at the sight of gold that they all just sat down next to the precious hoard. The worst of them spoke first. "Brothers," he said, "listen to what I am going to say. Even though I laugh at things and joke around, my mind is shrewd. Fortune has given this treasure to us so that we can live our lives in merriment and fun, and we should spend this money as easily as we came by it. But if this gold could be carried from this place to my home or yours—for we certainly know that all this gold is ours—then we would all be extremely happy. But we certainly cannot carry it home during the day because men would say that we were flagrant thieves, and they'd soon hang us for the taking of our own treasure. Thus, this gold must be carried away at night, as carefully and secretly as possible.

Therefore, I suggest that we all draw lots, and the person with the shortest straw should run off to town and secretly bring bread and wine back to us. The other two will closely guard the gold, and if it doesn't take too long, we can all carry away the treasure at night to a spot we agree is the best place."

Where, by agreement, we may think it best."
That one of them the cuts brought in his fist
190 And bade them draw to see where it might fall;
And it fell on the youngest of them all;
And so, forth toward the town he went anon.
And just as soon as he had turned and gone,
That one of them spoke thus unto the other:
195 "You know well that you are my own sworn brother,
So to your profit I will speak anon.
You know well how our comrade is just gone;
And here is gold, and that in great plenty,
That's to be parted here among us three.
200 Nevertheless, if I can shape it so
That it be parted only by us two,
Shall I not do a turn that is friendly?"
    The other said: "Well, now, how can that be?
He knows well that the gold is with us two.
205 What shall we say to him? What shall we do?"
    "Shall it be secret?" asked the first rogue, then,
"And I will tell you in eight words, or ten,
What we must do, and how bring it about."
    "Agreed," replied the other, "Never doubt,
210 That, on my word, I nothing will betray."
    "Now," said the first, "we're two, and I dare say
The two of us are stronger than is one.
Watch when he sits, and soon as that is done
Arise and make as if with him to play;
215 And I will thrust him through the two sides, yea,
The while you romp with him as in a game,
And with your dagger see you do the same;
And then shall all this gold divided be,
My right dear friend, just between you and me;
220 Then may we both our every wish fulfill
And play at dice all at our own sweet will."
And thus agreed were these two rogues, that day,
To slay the third, as you have heard me say.
    This youngest rogue who'd gone into the town,
225 Often in fancy rolled he up and down

They drew the lots and the youngest of them happened to pick the shortest. So, immediately he started off toward town.

Just as soon as he had turned and gone, one of the two said to the other, "You well know that you are my sworn brother, so I will speak to you about something profitable. You well know that our friend is gone, and here is a great amount of gold which is going to be divided between the three of us. But if I could figure out how to divide it only between the two of us, wouldn't I be doing you a good turn?"

The other answered, "Well, now, how can that be? He knows that the gold is with us. What shall we tell him? What shall we do?"

"Will you keep a secret?" asked the first rogue. "I will tell you in a few words what we must do and how we are going to do it."

"Agreed," replied the other. "On my word, I will reveal nothing. Don't you worry."

"Now," said the first, "there are two of us, and we know that we two are stronger than one. Watch when the other returns, and once he sits down, right away you get up as though you would fool with him; and I will stab him through both sides while you play with him as in a game. And with your dagger see that you do the same. Then, dear friend, all this gold shall be divided just between you and me. Then we may both fulfill our every wish and play at dice whenever we will." And so these two scoundrels agreed that day to kill the third, as you heard me say.

The youngest scoundrel who'd gone into the town imagined handling the beautiful new, bright gold coins. "Oh Lord," he thought, "if

171

The beauty of those florins new and bright.
"O Lord," thought he, "if so be that I might
Have all this treasure to myself alone,
There is no man who lives beneath the throne
230 Of God that should be then so merry as I."
    And at the last the Fiend, our enemy,
Put in his thought that he should poison buy
With which he might kill both his fellows; aye,
The Devil found him in such wicked state,
235 He had full leave his grief to consummate;
For it was utterly the man's intent
To kill them both and never to repent.
And on he strode, no longer would he tarry,
Into the town, to an apothecary,
240 And prayed of him that he'd prepare and sell
Some poison for his rats, and some as well
For a polecat that in his yard had lain,
The which, he said, his capons there had slain,
And fain he was to rid him, if he might,
245 Of vermin that thus damaged him by night.
The apothecary said: "And you shall have
A thing of which, so God my spirit save,
In all this world there is not live creature
That's eaten or has drunk of this mixture
250 As much as equals but a grain of wheat,
That shall not sudden death thereafter meet;
Yea, die he shall, and in a shorter while
Than you require to walk but one short mile;
This poison is so violent and strong."
255 This wicked man the poison took along
With him boxed up, and then he straightway ran
Into the street adjoining, to a man,
And of him borrowed generous bottles three;
And into two his poison then poured he;
260 The third one he kept clean for his own drink.
For all that night he was resolved to swink
In carrying the florins from that place.
And when this roisterer, with evil grace,
Had filled with wine his mighty bottles three,

I could have all that treasure to myself, there is no man alive who would be as happy as I."

And at the end, the Devil, our enemy, put in the young man's mind the idea that he should buy poison to kill both his companions. Because the Devil found him in such a wicked condition, he had full permission to carry out the young man's destruction; for it was absolutely the young man's intent to kill them both and never to repent. And on he walked quickly into the town to a druggist and asked him to prepare and sell him some poison with which he might kill some rats and a polecat that had come in his yard at night and killed his chickens.

The druggist said, "You will have something which, I swear, will cause sudden death to any creature who eats or drinks the mixture in an amount equal to a grain of wheat. Yes, this poison is so violent and strong that he shall die in a shorter time than it takes to walk one short mile."

This wicked man took along the poison in a box and ran immediately to the next street and borrowed three large bottles from a man. He poured the poison into two of the bottles, and the third he kept pure for his own drink. For he was prepared to work all that night carrying the gold coins from that place. And when this scoundrel, with an evil will, had filled the three large bottles with wine, he returned to his comrades.

265 Then to his comrades forth again went he.
What is the need to tell about it more?
For just as they had planned his death before,
Just so they murdered him, and that anon.
And when the thing was done, then spoke the one:
270 "Now let us sit and drink and so be merry,
And afterward we will his body bury."
And as he spoke, one bottle of the three
He took wherein the poison chanced to be
And drank and gave his comrade drink also,
275 For which, and that anon, lay dead these two.
Thus ended these two homicides in woe;
Died thus the treacherous poisoner also.
O cursed sin, full of abominableness!
O treacherous homicide! O wickedness!
280 O gluttony, lechery, and hazardry!
O blasphemer of Christ with villainy,
And with great oaths, habitual for pride!
Alas! Mankind, how may this thing betide
That to thy dear Creator, Who thee wrought,
285 And with His precious blood salvation bought,
Thou art so false and so unkind, alas!
Now, good men, God forgive you each trespass,
And keep you from the sin of avarice.
My holy pardon cures and will suffice,
290 So that it brings me gold, or silver brings,
Or else, I care not—brooches, spoons or rings.
Bow down your heads before this holy bull!
Come up, you wives, and offer of your wool!
Your names I'll enter on my roll, anon,
295 And into Heaven's bliss you'll go, each one.
For I'll absolve you, by my special power,
You that make offering, as clean this hour
As you were born.
　　　　And lo, sirs, thus I preach.
300 And Jesus Christ, who is our souls' great leech,
So grant you each his pardon to receive;
For that is best; I will not you deceive.

There is no need to tell what happened next. They killed him quickly, just as they had planned in advance. And when the deed was done, one of them said, "Now let us drink and have fun, and later we will bury his body."

And as he spoke, he took one of the three bottles which, by chance, contained the poison. He drank and also gave some to his friend, which caused them to both died instantly. Therefore, these two murders ended in misery, and the treacherous poisoner died also.

O cursed sin, full of hate! O treacherous murder! O wickedness! O gluttony, lust, and gambling! O he who swears against Christ with great and vile oaths out of habit and pride! Alas! Mankind, how can it be that you are so false and unkind to the dear Creator who made you and bought you salvation with His precious blood. Now good men, God forgive you each sin and keep you from the sin of avarice. My holy pardon can save you if you have any gold or silver to bring, or anything else, I don't care—brooches, spoons, or rings. Come on, you women, offer your wool. I will write your name down on my rolls and into the bliss of Heaven each of you will go. By my special power, I will pardon you who give offering and make you as pure this hour as the day you were born.

And see, sirs, thus I preach.
And Jesus Christ, who is our souls' great physician, so grant you each to receive his pardon, for that is best; I will not deceive you.

But, sirs, one word forgot I in my tale;
I've relics in my pouch that cannot fail,
305 As good as England ever saw, I hope,
The which I got by kindness of the pope.
If gifts your change of heart and mind reveal.
You'll get my absolution while you kneel.
Come forth, and kneel down here before, anon.
310 And humbly you'll receive my full pardon;
Or else receive a pardon as you wend,
All new and fresh as every mile shall end,
So that you offer me each time, anew,
More gold and silver, all good coins and true.
315 It is an honour to each one that's here
That you may have a competent pardoner
To give you absolution as you ride,
For all adventures that may still betide.
Perchance from horse may fall down one or two,
320 Breaking his neck, and it might well be you.
See what insurance, then, it is for all
That I within your fellowship did fall,
Who may absolve you, both the great and less,
When soul from body passes, as I guess.
325 I think our host might just as well begin,
For he is most enveloped in all sin.
Come forth, sir host, and offer first anon,
And you shall kiss the relics, every one,
Aye, for a groat! Unbuckle now your purse."
330 "Nay, nay," said he, "then may I have Christ's curse!
Why, you would have me kissing your old breeches,
And swear they were the relics of a saint,
Though with your excrement 'twere dabbed like paint.
By cross Saint Helen found in Holy Land,
335 I would I had your ballocks in my hand
Instead of relics in a reliquary;
Let's cut them off, and them I'll help you carry;
They shall be shrined within a hog's fat turd."
This pardoner, he answered not a word;
340 So wrathy was he no word would he say.

But sirs, one thing I forgot in my tale. I have relics in my pouch that cannot fail. They are the best England ever saw, I hope, and were given to me by the kindness of the pope. If your gifts reveal your change of heart and mind, you'll get my pardon while you kneel. Come forth, and kneel down here before me now and humbly receive my full pardon, or else receive a new pardon at the end of each mile as we travel, as long as you offer me more gold and silver each time.

It is an honor to each one who's here that you have a competent pardoner to grant you forgiveness for anything that may happen on the way as you ride. Perhaps one or two of you may fall from a horse and break your neck. See what a safeguard it is for everyone that I happened to join your company so that I might pardon you, both the high and the low, when the soul passes from the body. I suggest that our host be the first one to seek the pardon because he is the most surrounded by sin. Come forth, sir host, and make the first offering, and you shall kiss every one of the relics, yes, for a grain of oats. Open your purse now!

"No, no," said the innkeeper, "then may I have Christ's curse. You would have me kiss your old pants and swear they were the relics of a saint even though they were stained like paint with your excrement. But by the cross which Saint Helen found in the Holy Land, I would rather have your testicles in my hand than the relics in a relic-box. Let's cut them off, and I will help you carry them; they shall be enshrined in a hog's fat turd." This pardoner could not say anything in reply; he was too angry to open his mouth.

"Now," said our host, "I will no longer play
With you, nor any other angry man."
But at this point the worthy knight began,
When that he saw how all the folk did laugh:
345   "No more of this, for it's gone far enough;
Sir pardoner, be glad and merry here;
And you, sir host, who are to me so dear,
I pray you that you kiss the pardoner.
And, pardoner, I pray you to draw near,
350   And as we did before, let's laugh and play."
And then they kissed and rode forth on their way.

"Now," said our host, "I will no longer play with you or any other angry man."

But at this point, when he saw how everyone laughed, the worthy knight began, "No more of this, for it's gone far enough. Sir pardoner, be glad and happy here; and you, sir host, who means so much to me, I ask that you kiss the pardoner. And, pardoner, I ask you to draw near and let's laugh and play as we did before." And then they kissed and rode forth on their way.

Comprehension Check

1. Considering the way the pardoner himself is portrayed, what might Chaucer be criticizing about the Catholic church during this period?

2. How do the three rioters conceive of Death?

3. How does the old man appear to think of Death?

4. In light of later events, what is ironic about the oath the rioters swear?

5. How are we meant to interpret the rioters' seeking out Death under the tree to which the old man directed them?

6. What action occurs after the deaths of the rioters, and how would you characterize it?

The Wife of Bath's Prologue

In this tale and its prologue, Chaucer satirizes those aspects of society that involve male/female relationships. The Wife of Bath has been married five times, and, in the first four marriages, she tells us that she had dominated the relationship through guile and sex. By her fifth marriage, not so young and not so pretty as she used to be, she runs into some problems. This is where we pick up her story.

'Now will I tell you truth, by Saint Thomas
Of why I tore from out his book a leaf
For which he struck me so it made me deaf.
    "He had a book that gladly, night and day
5   For his amusement he would read alway.
He called it 'Theophrastus' and 'Valeriou',
At which book would he laugh uproarious
And every night and day 'twas his custom,
When he had leisure and took some vacation
10   From all his other worldly occupation,
To read, within this book, of wicked wives.
He knew of them more legends and more lives
Than are of good wives written in the Bible.
For trust me, it's impossible, no libel,
15   That any cleric shall speak well of wives,
Unless it be of saints and holy lives,
But naught for other women will they do.
By God, if women had but written stories,
As have these clerks within their oratories,
20   They would have written of men more wickedness
Than all the race of Adam could redress.
Therefore no woman by a clerk is praised.
A clerk, when he is old and can naught do
Of Venus' labours worth his worn-out shoe,
25   Then sits he down and writes, in his dotage,
That women cannot keep vow of marriage!

The Wife of Bath's Prologue

By St. Thomas, now I tell you why I tore a page from his book and how he struck me so hard it made me deaf.

He had a book he enjoyed reading. Within this book were stories of wicked wives. He knew many more stories of wicked wives than of the good wives written about in the Bible. For it's impossible for any priest to speak well of wives unless they are saints, but they will do nothing for other women. By God, if women were to write stories as the priests had done, they would have written of more wickedness by men than all the sons of Adam could correct.

Therefore, no woman is ever praised by a cleric. A cleric, when he is old and can no longer make love, sits down and writes that women cannot keep their marriage vows.

"But now to tell you, as I started to,
Why I was beaten for a book, *pardieu*.
Upon a night Jenkin, who was our sire,
30   Read in his book, as he sat by the fire,
Of Mother Eve who, by her wickedness,
First brought mankind to all his wretchedness
For which Lord Jesus Christ Himself was slain,
Who, with His heart's blood, saved us thus again.
35   Lo here, expressly of woman, may you find
That woman was the ruin of mankind.
Then read he out how Samson lost his hairs
When sleeping, his mistress cut them with her shears;
And through this treason lost he either eye.
40   And nothing escaped him of the pain and woe
That Socrates had with his spouses two;"
"Of Clytemnestra, for her lechery,
Who caused her husband's death by treachery,
He read all thus with greatest zest, I vow.
45   "Of Livia and Lucia told he me,
For both of them their husbands killed, you see,
The one for love, the other killed for hate;
Then did he tell how one Latumius
Complained unto his comrade Arrius
50   That in his garden grew a baleful tree
Whereon, he said, his wives, and they were three,
Had hanged themselves for wretchedness and woe.
'Of brother,' Arrius said, 'and did they so?
Give me a graft of that same blessed tree
55   And in my garden planted it shall be!'
Of wives of later date he also read,
How some had slain their husbands in their bed
And let their lovers shag them all the night
While corpses lay upon the floor upright.
60   And some had driven nails into the brain
While husbands slept and in such wise were slain.
And some had given them poison in their drink.
He told more evil than the mind can think.
And therewithal he knew of more proverbs
65   Than in this world there grows of grass or herbs.
'Better,' he said, 'your habitation be

But to return to my story, I'll tell you why I was beaten for a book, by God. One night my husband sat reading about Mother Eve, who by her wickedness, brought sin into the world. As of result of her actions, Jesus Christ died to save us.

So we find that a woman was the ruin of mankind. Then he read of how Samson lost his hair by his mistress and wound up blind through treason.

And nothing escaped him about the pain and woe Socrates had because of his two wives.

He told of Clytemnestra, who killed her husband because of her own lechery. And he read with great zest of Livia and Lucia, both of whom killed their husbands.

Then he told of how when Latumius complained to his comrade Arrius about a tree in his yard that three of his wives had hanged themselves from; Arrius asked if he could have a graft from that tree.

He also read of other wives, who had slain their husbands in their bed and then spent the night with their lovers in that bed while the husband's corpse lay on the floor. Some hammered nails into their sleeping husband's brain; some were poisoned with drink. He told of more evil than the mind can think of.

And he knew many apt proverbs, more than there are blades of grass. "Better you live with a lion or dragon than with a woman

With lion wild or dragon foul,' said he,
'Than with a woman who will nag and chide.'
'Better,' he said, 'on the housetop abide
70   Than with a brawling wife down in the house;
Such are so wicked and contrarious
They hate the thing their husband loves, for aye.'
"And when I saw he'd never cease, in fine,
His reading in this cursed book at night,
75   Three leaves of it I snatched and tore outright
Out of his book, as he read on; and also
I with my fist so took him on the cheek
That in our fire he reeled and fell right down.
Then he got up as does a wild lion,
80   And with his fist he struck me on the head,
And on the floor I lay as I were dead.
And when he saw how limp and still I lay,
He was afraid and would have run away,
Until at last out of my swoon I made:
85   'Oh, have you slain me, you false thief?' I said,
'And for my land have you thus murdered me?
Kiss me before I die, and let me be.'"
     "He came to me and near me he knelt down,
And said: 'O my dear Alison,
90   So help me God, I'll never strike you more;
What I have done, you are to blame therefor.
But all the same forgiveness now I seek!'
And thereupon I hit him on the cheek,
And said: 'Thief, so much vengeance do I wreak
95   Now will I die, I can no longer speak!'
But at the last, and with much care and woe,
We made it up between ourselves. And so
He put the bridle reins within my hand
To have the governing of house and land;
100   And of his tongue and of his hand, also;
And I made him burn his book, right then, oho!
And when I had thus gathered unto me
Masterfully, the entire sovereignty,
And he had said: 'My own true wedded wife,
105   Do as you please the term of all your life.'"

who nags you," or "Better you live on the roof than inside the house with a wicked wife who is always finding a reason to fight. Contrarian wives hate what their husbands love."

And when I saw he'd never stop with this, I snatched the book from his hand and tore the pages from it, and with my fist I hit him on the cheek and knocked him down. Like a wild lion he got up and hit me on the head so hard that I fell and lay on the floor like I was dead. He was so frightened he was about to run off when I said, "Oh you've murdered me for my land; kiss me before I die."

He knelt beside me and sought my forgiveness and swore that he would never strike me again. Then I hit him on the cheek and said, "That's all the revenge I want; now I'll die." But at last we made up and he put the bridles in my hand, so now I govern house, land, his tongue, and his hand. I also made him burn his book. And when I had gathered all the power to my rule, he said, "My true wife, do as you wish all your life."

The Tale of the Wife of Bath

NOW IN THE OLDEN days of King Arthur,
Of whom the Britons speak with great honour,
All this wide land was land of faery.
The elfqueen, with her jolly company,
5   Danced oftentimes on many a green mead;
This was the old opinion, as I read.
But now no man can see the elves, you know.
For now the so-great charity and prayers
Of limiters and other holy friars
10   That do infest each land and every stream
As thick as motes are in a bright sunbeam,
Blessing halls, chambers, kitchens, ladies bowers,
Cities and towns and castles and high towers,
Manors and barns and stables, aye and dairies—
15   This causes it that there are now no fairies.
For where was wont to walk full many an elf,
Right there walks now the limiter himself
In noons and afternoons and in mornings,
Saying his matins and such holy things,
20   As he goes round his district in his gown.
Women may now go safely up and down,
In every copse or under every tree;
There is no other incubus than he,
And would do them nothing but dishonour.
25   And so befell it that this King Arthur
Had at his court a lusty bachelor
Who, on a day, came riding from river;
And happened that, alone as she was born,
He saw a maiden walking through the corn,
30   From whom, in spite of all she did and said,
Straightway by force he took her maidenhead;
For which violation was there such clamour,

The Tale of the Wife of Bath

In the olden days of the much honored King Arthur, the entire country was filled with fairies, at which time the elf-queen with her court used to dance over the green fields. At least that was the opinion, so I've read; but, now, no one can see elves anymore, because of the many prayers of the holy friars. These holy friars infest and bless every stream and land and, as a result, there are no more fairies. Where elves once walked, the priests themselves now walk daily, saying their prayers as they go about their business. Women now may safely travel around because there is not an enticing spirit left in any bush or tree to dishonor them.

And so it happened that King Arthur had a lusty, young knight in his court. One day, the knight came riding by the river and happened to see a young woman walking alone ahead of him. Even though she told him to stay away, he approached her and by sheer force he raped her. The people, demanding justice for this crime, appealed to King Arthur, who decided that the knight should be executed according to the law at the time.

And such appealing unto King Arthur,
That soon condemned was this knight to be dead
35 By course of law, and should have lost his head,
Peradventure, such being the statute then;
But that the other ladies and the queen
So long prayed of the king to show him grace,
He granted life, at last, in the law's place,
40 And gave him to the queen, as she should will,
Whether she'd save him, or his blood should spill.
    The queen she thanked the king with all her might,
And after this, thus spoke she to the knight,
When she'd an opportunity, one day:
45 "You stand yet," said she, "in such poor a way
That for your life you've no security.
I'll grant you life if you can tell to me
What thing it is that women most desire.
Be wise, and keep your neck from iron dire!
50 And if you cannot tell it me anon,
Then will I give you license to be gone
A twelvemonth and a day, to search and learn
Sufficient answer in this grave concern.
And your knight's word I'll have, ere forth you pace,
55 To yield your body to me in this place."
    And so he took his leave and went his way.
He sought out every house and every place
Wherein he hoped to find that he had grace
To learn what women love the most of all;
60 But nowhere ever did it him befall
To find, upon the question stated here,
Two persons who agreed with statement clear.
    Some said that women all loved best riches,
Some said, fair fame, and some said, prettiness;
65 Some, rich array, some said 'twas lust abed
And often to be widowed and re-wed.
    Some said that our poor hearts are aye most eased
When we have been most flattered and thus pleased.
And he went near the truth, I will not lie;
70 A man may win us best with flattery;
And with attentions and with busyness

But the queen and other ladies of the court begged the king for mercy. After listening to their pleas, the king decided to let the knight live, but he turned the knight's punishment over to the queen. Thus it was for her to decide what would happen to the knight, whether he would live or die.

The queen thanked the king with all of her might, and then spoke this to the knight. "You still may die, but I will grant you life if you can tell me what one thing do women desire most of all? Be careful if you want to keep your neck from being chopped off. If you cannot tell me the answer right now, I will let you have twelve months to search and learn an acceptable answer to this question. Before you leave, however, you must give me your oath as a knight that you will return here in twelve months."

The knight left and accepted his fate and traveled into the country to make his search. He sought at every house along the way, and anywhere else he thought he might find the answer to what it is that women desire most of all. In all of his travels, however, he never came to a place where he could find two people who agreed on the subject.

Some said that women desire money the most. Some said a good reputation; some said beauty; some said fine clothes, some said lust in bed and to be widowed often so that they might remarry.

Some said that a woman's spirits were most calmed when they were flattered and pleased. And I must say, that answer comes close to the truth, for a man may win us best with flattery and much attention.

We're often limed, the greater and the less.
    And some folk say that great delight have we
To be held constant, also trustworthy,
75 And on one purpose steadfastly to dwell,
And not betray a thing that men may tell.
But that tale is not worth a rake's handle,
For God knows, we women can no thing conceal.
    When what the knight went for he could not find out,
80 That is, the thing that women love the best,
Most saddened was the spirit in his breast;
But home he goes, he could no more delay.
The day was come when home he turned his way;
And on his way it chanced that he should ride
85 In all his care, beneath a forest's side,
And there he saw, a-dancing him before,
Full four and twenty ladies, maybe more;
Toward which dance eagerly did he turn
In hope that there some wisdom he should learn.
90 But truly, ere he came upon them there,
The dancers vanished all, he knew not where.
No creature saw he that gave sign of life,
Save, on the greensward sitting, an old wife;
A fouler person could no man devise.
95 Before the knight this old wife did arise,
And said: "Sir knight, hence lies no travelled way.
Tell me what thing you seek, and by your fay,
Perchance you'll find it may the better be;
These ancient folk know many things," said she.
100   "Dear mother," said this knight assuredly
"I am but dead, save I can tell, truly,
What thing it is that women most desire;
Could you inform me, I'd pay well your hire."
    "Plight me your troth here, hand in hand," said she,
105 "That you will do, whatever it may be,
The thing I ask if it lie in your might;
And I'll give you your answer ere the night."
    "Have here my word," said he. "That thing I grant."
    "Then," said the crone, "of this I make my vaunt,
110 Your life is safe; and I will stand thereby,

Some people say that women love to be considered dependable, trustworthy, and not likely to tell secrets, but that idea is worthless, for it is well known that women cannot keep a secret.

When the knight could not find out that for which he searched, he became saddened realizing that he was not going to find an answer to the queen's question. Finally, the day came when he would have to return to the queen's court without more delay. On his way, as he rode near a forest, he happened to see a group of ladies, twenty-four or more, dancing in a circle. Riding quickly toward them, he hoped that he might learn something. Just before he reached them, however, the dancers vanished. No creature was around except for an old woman sitting on the grass. And you can't imagine an uglier old woman than this one. This woman stood up and said, "Sir knight, no road goes through this forest; what is it you are seeking? It may be that I can help you, for old people know many things."

"Dear mother," said the knight, "I am certainly dead unless I can tell what one thing women most desire. If you could tell me that, I could repay you for your trouble."

"Make a promise to me," she said, "that the next thing I ask you to do, you will do it if it lies within your power. If you do so, I will tell you the answer before night comes."

"You have my word," said the knight, "that I will grant what you wish."
Then, the old lady said, "I swear to you that your life is safe,

Upon my life, the queen will say as I.
Let's see which is the proudest of them all
That wears upon her hair kerchief or caul,
Shall dare say no to that which I shall teach;
115   Let us go now and without longer speech."
    Then whispered she a sentence in his ear,
And bade him to be glad and have no fear.
When they were come unto the court, this knight
Said he had kept his promise as was right,
120   And ready was his answer, as he said.
Full many a noble wife, and many a maid,
And many a widow, since they are so wise,
The queen herself sitting as high justice,
Assembled were, his answer there to hear;
125   And then the knight was bidden to appear.
    Command was given for silence in the hall,
And that the knight should tell before them all
What thing all worldly women love the best.
This knight did not stand dumb, as does a beast,
130   But to this question presently answered
With manly voice, so that the whole court heard:
    "My liege lady, generally," said he,
"Women desire to have the sovereignty
As well upon their husband as their love,
135   And to have mastery their man above;
This thing you most desire, though me you kill
Do as you please, I am here at your will."
    In all the court there was no wife or maid
Or widow that denied the thing he said,
140   But all held, he was worthy to have life.
    And with that word up started the old wife
Whom he had seen a-sitting on the green.
"Mercy," cried she, "my sovereign lady queen!
Before the court's dismissed, give me my right.
145   'Twas I who taught the answer to this knight;
For which he did plight troth to me, out there,
That the first thing I should of him require
He would do that, if it lay in his might.
Before the court, now, pray I you, sir knight,"
150   Said she, "that you will take me for your wife;

for the queen will say as I say; none of those ladies at court in their bonnets will dare deny that which I say to you. Without further talk, let us now go to the queen."

Then she whispered a sentence in his ear and told him to have no fear. When they came into the court, the knight said he had kept his promise and was ready to answer the question. Assembled there were many a noble wife and many a maid, and many a widow with the queen herself sitting as high justice; all were there to hear his answer. And then the knight was bidden to appear.

A command was given for silence in the hall, and that the knight should tell what thing all worldly women love the best. This knight did not stand silent as a beast, but answered the question with a manly voice, so that the whole court heard.

"My queen, generally speaking," he said, "women desire to have the same sovereignty over their husband that they had over their lover and to be master of them. This is your greatest desire. Kill me, or do with me as you please. I am at your mercy."

Through the court there was no woman who would deny what he had said, and they all agreed that the knight deserved to live.

With that, the old woman the knight had seen on the grass jumped up. "Thank you," she cried, "my sovereign lady queen! Before this court adjourns, grant me justice. I taught this knight the answer. In exchange, he promised to do the first thing I told him to do, if it was within his power. In front of the court, I ask you, sir knight, to take me as your wife. It is clear that I saved your life. If I am lying, say so right now!"

For well you know that I have saved your life.
If this be false, say nay, upon your fay!"
    This knight replied: "Alas and welaway!
That I so promised I will not protest.
155   But for God's love pray make a new request,
Take all my wealth and let my body go."
    "Nay then," said she, "beshrew us if I do!
For though I may be foul and old and poor,
I will not, for all metal and all ore
160   That from the earth is dug or lies above,
Be aught except your wife and your true love."
    "My love?" cried he, "nay, rather my damnation!
Alas! that any of my race and station
Should ever so dishonoured foully be!"
165   But all for naught; the end was this, that he
Was so constrained he needs must go and wed,
And take his ancient wife and go to bed.
    Great was the woe the knight had in his thought
When he, with her, to marriage bed was brought;
170   He rolled about and turned him to and fro.
His old wife lay there, always smiling so,
And said: "O my dear husband, *ben'cite*!
Fares every knight with wife as you with me?
Is this the custom in King Arthur's house?
175   Are knights of his all so fastidious?
I am your own true love and, more, your wife;
And I am she who saved your very life;
And truly, since I've never done you wrong,
Why do you treat me so, this first night long?
180   You act as does a man who's lost his wit;
What is my fault? For God's love tell me it,
And it shall be amended, if I may."
    "Amended!" cried this knight, "Alas, nay, nay!
It will not be amended ever, no!
185   You are so loathsome, and so old also,
And therewith of so low a race were born,
It's little wonder that I toss and turn.
Would God my heart would break within my breast!"
    "Is this," asked she, "the cause of your unrest?"
190   "Yes, truly," said he, "and no wonder 'tis."

The knight replied, "No it is true; I remember my promise, but for God's sake, please choose another request. Take everything I own, but leave my body."

"No," said the old woman, "though I be old and poor I would not take all of the gold on earth in exchange for being your wife and your love."

"My love?" he cried. "No, I am doomed. Never was any of my race or position so dishonored."

His protests were, however, all for nothing, because his promise compelled him to marry her. Thus he took his old wife and went with her to the marriage bed.

So great was the knight's sorrow and his mind so troubled, that in bed he rolled around and turned this way and that. All this time his wife just lay smiling and said, "O, dear husband, bless you; does every knight act this way with his wife? Is this the custom for married people in court? Are all his knights so timid? I am your wife, your love, the one who saved your life. Why, since I've done you no wrong, do you treat me so? Why do you act like a man who has lost his mind? If I have done something wrong, tell me what it is so I can fix it."

"Fix it?" he said. "No, it cannot be fixed. You are repulsive and old and born of low parents. It is no wonder that I toss and turn. By God, my heart breaks within my breast."

"Is this," asked she, "what is causing all the trouble?"
"Yes, truly, it is," said he, "and it is no wonder."

"Now, sir," said she, "I could amend all this,
If I but would, and that within days three,
If you would bear yourself well towards me.
But since you speak of such gentility
195 As is descended from old wealth, till ye
Claim that for that you should be gentlemen,
I hold such arrogance not worth a hen.
Find him who is most virtuous alway,
Alone or publicly, and most tries aye
200 To do whatever noble deeds he can,
And take him for the greatest gentleman.
Christ wills we claim from Him gentility,
Not from ancestors of landocracy."
    "And when you me reproach for poverty,
205 The High God, in Whom we believe, say I,
In voluntary poverty lived His life.
And surely every man, or maid, or wife
May understand that Jesus, Heaven's King,
Would not have chosen vileness of living.
210 Glad poverty's an honest thing, that's plain,
Which Seneca and other clerks maintain.
Whoso will be content with poverty,
I hold him rich, though not a shirt has he.
And he that covets much is a poor wight,
215 For he would gain what's all beyond his might.
But he that has not, nor desires to have,
Is rich, although you hold him but a knave."
    "Now, sir, with age you have upbraided me;
Now since you say that I am foul and old,
220 Then fear you not to be made of a cuckold;
For dirt and age, as prosperous I may be,
Are mighty wardens over chastity.
Nevertheless, since I know your delight,
I'll satisfy your wordly appetite."
225   "Choose, now," said she, "one of these two things, aye,
To have me foul and old until I die,
And be to you a true and humble wife,
And never anger you in all my life;
Or else to have me young and very fair
230 And take your chance with those who will repair

198

"Now, sir," said she, "I could fix all of this within three days if I felt like it, and if you behaved nicely to me. But since you speak of that gentility that is derived from old wealth and allows one to call himself a gentleman, I hold that point of view to be worthless arrogance. He who is most virtuous, both when alone or in public, and does what noble deeds he can, I take him for the greatest gentleman. For Christ wills that we look to him for gentility, not to our ancestors or our wealth.

"And when you reproach me for my poverty, I say that Christ lived his life in voluntary poverty and surely everyone understands that Jesus would not have chosen vileness as a way of life. Poverty is an honest way of life, and as Seneca and other writers maintain, he who is content with his poverty is rich, though he may not own a shirt. But he who desires much wealth is a poor figure, for he can't gain what is beyond his power. But he that hasn't much wealth, nor desires to have it, is rich, although you may think him a knave.

"Now, sir, you have unkindly mentioned my old age, but consider this. Since as you say, I'm old and foul, you need not fear that other men will take me to bed, for dirt and age are protectors of one's virginity. Nevertheless, since I know what delights you, I shall fulfill your desire for me to be more beautiful."

"You have to choose, however, between these two. Am I to be an ugly, old, but good and faithful wife, or am I to be a beautiful, young wife who may lie with other men? Now, choose the one that you like better."

Unto your house, and all because of me,
Or in some other place, as well may be.
Now choose which you like better and reply."
    This knight considered, and did sorely sigh,
235 But at the last replied as you shall hear:
"My lady and my love, and wife so dear,
I put myself in your wise governing;
Do you choose which may be the more pleasing,
And bring most honour to you, and me also.
240 I care not which it be of these things two;
For if you like it, that suffices me."
    "Then have I got of you the mastery,
Since I may choose and govern, in earnest?"
    "Yes, truly, wife," said he, "I hold that best."
245   "Kiss me," said she, "we'll be no longer wroth,
For by my truth, to you I will be both;
That is to say, I'll be both good and fair.
I pray God I go mad, and so declare,
If I be not to you as good and true
250 As ever wife was since the world was new.
And, save I be, at dawn, as fairly seen
As any lady, empress, or great queen
That is between the east and the far west,
Do with my life and death as you like best.
255 Throw back the curtain and see how it is."
    And when the knight saw verily all this,
That she so very fair was, and young too,
For joy he clasped her in his strong arms two,
His heart bathed in a bath of utter bliss;
260 A thousand times, all in a row, he'd kiss.
And she obeyed his wish in everything.
    And thus they lived unto their lives' fair end,
In perfect joy; and Jesus to us send
Meek husbands, and young ones, fresh in bed,
265 And good luck to outlive them that we wed.
And I pray Jesus to cut short the lives
Of those who'll not be governed by their wives;
And old and querulous niggards with their pence,
And send them soon a mortal pestilence!

The knight thought about this and sighed; at last he answered: "My lady, my love, my dear wife, I will do what you think is best. You choose whichever you think will bring us the most pleasure and the most honor to our marriage. I don't care which of the two you choose, for as long as it satisfies you, it satisfies me!"

"Then may I really choose and run things as I decide?"
"Yes," he said, "I think it best."

"Kiss me," she said. "We will no longer be at odds, because I promise to be both to you. That is to say, I will be both beautiful and good. And I pray to God that if I'm not as good and true a wife as ever was since time began, may I go mad. And if I'm also not as beautiful as any lady, empress, or great queen, you may do with my life or death as you think best. Throw back the curtain and look at me now."

When the knight did this, he saw that his wife was very young and beautiful. For joy, he clasped her in his arms. With his heart bathed in this bliss, a thousand times he kissed her. She, in turn, obeyed his wish in everything.

Thus they happily lived out their lives. May Jesus send to us meek husbands who are young and fresh in bed, and may we have the good luck to outlive them. Those who will not be governed by their wives, I pray that Jesus cut short their lives. While for the old and quarrelsome husband, who is stingy with his money, may Jesus send him a deadly plague.

Comprehension Check

Prologue to the Wife of Bath's Tale

1. What does the opening stanza tell us about Dame Alice's present husband?

2. Why do clerics say that "woman was the ruin of mankind"?

3. The major theme of the prologue and tale is the battle of the sexes. Can you think of a social-historical context in which this might be the case?

4. How does Alice gain mastery over her husband?

Questions for Essay or Discussion

1. Many critics find Dame Alice a very interesting character, but they have different opinions about her motivation and character. What is your opinion of Alice?

2. What do you suppose Chaucer's opinion of women might have been?

3. Critics point out that this tale, along with its prologue, is all about "choices" and being in control of one's own life. How much of that do you see?

The Tale of the Wife of Bath

1. Why is the opening an important part of this story?

2. Why is it ironic that considering the knight's crime, the queen is to be the one to decide his fate?

3. Under what condition does the queen say the knight may save his life?

4. After fruitlessly searching for his answer for a year, from whom does the knight finally get an answer to his question? What promise must the knight make before he gets the answer?

5. Very reluctantly, the knight keeps his promise to the old hag, but what does he refuse to do?

6. Summarize what his new wife tells the knight about poverty, gentility, and ugliness.

7. What choice does the old hag offer the knight? What choice does the knight make and with what result?

8. What is the obvious relationship in the moral of this tale, and the point of Dame Alice's prologue?

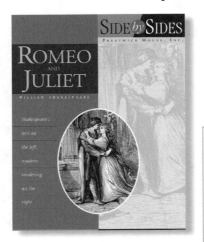